EVERYTHING
YOU WANT TO KNOW ABOUT
OWLS

EVERYTHING
YOU WANT TO KNOW ABOUT
OWLS

Dilys Breese

MIDSUMMER BOOKS

Published by:
Midsummer Books Ltd
179 Dalling Road
London W6 0ES
England
Telephone: 0181-749 2425
Fax: 0181-749 6249

Publisher: Stan Morse
Author: Dilys Breese
Introduction by: Paul Sterry
Consultant editors: Pat Morris,
Paul Sterry
Chris Mead
Editors: Rose Catt
Karen Frazer
Design: Sharon Wallis
Artist: John Ridyard
Photographer: Paul Bricknell

First published 1998

ISBN 1 900732 05 X

Printed in Itlay

CONTENTS

All about owls – by night and day

Steeped in folklore and superstition, owls are among the best-loved birds in Britain. We are fortunate to have six species on our doorstep, five of which are relatively easy to see.

The little owl is one of the easiest owl species to see, being active both by day and night.

Few owl species are more aptly named than the barn owl, which often nests in farm buildings such as barns.

A S THE SUN SETS AND THE DAILY activity of diurnal (active during the day) birds of prey winds down, the onset of darkness heralds the start of activity for most species of owls. In common with their diurnal counterparts they are voracious predators whose senses are honed to enable them to hunt in low light levels. Their prey includes small mammals and invertebrates.

With most species of owl, anyone wishing to study these amazing birds in their element must adopt nocturnal habits themselves, and concentrate their efforts during the hours of darkness. It soon becomes apparent that an appreciation of owl behaviour can also aid the birdwatcher: the virtues of patience and silence, for example, frequently reward both owls and owl-watchers with views of their elusive quarry. Observing owls in the wild has its obvious rewards but is not necessarily a pursuit for the faint-hearted. The bloodcurdling scream of a barn owl or the eerie sight of a tawny owl silhouetted against a moonlit sky can still send shivers down the spines of some of the most seasoned birdwatchers.

Britain is fortunate in having five species of owl that are resident and relatively widely distributed given the limitations of their habitat requirements. These are the barn, tawny, little, long-eared and short-eared owls. A further species, the snowy owl, is an

An owl has forward-facing eyes which are fixed in their sockets. Their hooked beaks are an essential requirement for tearing up prey.

Catching a glimpse of owls, let alone seeing them well, is notoriously difficult. Like other birds, owls are often easiest to find during the breeding season, although most birdwatchers refrain from trying to find birds at the nest. This is partly on account of the inevitable disturbance this causes, and because of their justified reputations for fearless defence of their offspring. It should also be kept in mind that barn and snowy owls are protected by law against disturbance at the nest.

Outside the breeding season you can look for strictly nocturnal species at daytime roosts. Tawny owls often roost in the cover provided by ivy growing on a tree trunk, and although an individual bird may use several different sites it will probably use the same location every few days. The owls are not easily disturbed, so scan any likely looking site carefully. You can also scan the ground for tell-tale pellets, coughed-up after a night's feeding. Long-eared owls occasionally roost communally during the winter and often favour hawthorn scrub or even conifer plantations. As a rule of thumb, you are unlikely to find long-eared owls in woodland areas where tawnies occur, as the species compete with one another.

Being at least partly diurnal, little owls can often be found perched on fence posts or dead branches in daylight. Listen out for the far-carrying, cat-like calls, often delivered in duet, as a sign of the bird's presence in an area. Short-eared owls also feed in the daytime, quartering grassy areas in search of small mammals. They are perhaps easiest to see in winter, when coastal marshes are a favourite haunt. Although largely nocturnal, barn owls often feed at dusk, and in suitable feeding areas such as grassy fields the same bird will often reappear to feed at a similar hour for several days running.

Tawny owls are entirely nocturnal and spend the daylight hours roosting in dense foliage.

Many owl species rely on patience and a wait-and-see approach to hunting. This little owl is scanning the ground from an overhanging branch.

irregular and rare breeder on the northern isles and also occurs as a rare winter vagrant further south in Britain. Although their nocturnal habits limit our ability to observe much of owl behaviour, two of our regularly occurring species are at least partly diurnal, providing wonderful opportunities for the birdwatcher.

For most people, their limited experience of seeing owls in the wild comes from tantalisingly brief views of birds caught in car headlights as they fly across country roads. Apart from the obvious problems associated with watching birds that, in the case of most species, are essentially nocturnal in habits, most owls are somewhat retiring by nature. There are ways of greatly improving your chances of observation however, and in common with other branches of natural history, the enterprising birdwatcher soon learns that a knowledge and understanding of the subject's habits and lifestyles are a great help. By providing details of everything from field identification to breeding behaviour, the information contained in this book will help to give the reader a thorough insight into the lives of these magnificent birds. The vivid illustrations are an additional celebration of our wonderful owls.

SO WHAT ARE OWLS?

There can be few people, young or old, who cannot recognise an owl when they see one. Although there is considerable size variation between the species found in Britain, all share characteristics which betray their family ties and allegiances. Typical owl traits include a disproportionately large head with a rounded outline, a flattened facial disc surrounding large, staring eyes, and a body that is usually comparatively dumpy. Although owls are predatory birds, they are not closely related to diurnal birds of prey such as falcons and hawks. While most owl species share a similar diet to raptors such as kestrels and buzzards (which eat small mammals and invertebrates), confrontation between the two groups is generally avoided as they feed at different times of day. Unrelated they may be, but both owls and raptors have acquired common characteristics to suit their shared predatory lifestyles. Both have sharp talons for capturing and killing their prey, and hooked bills for tearing the flesh for their chicks. Biologists refer to the process by which both groups of birds acquired these physical attributes as 'convergent evolution'.

OWL CLASSIFICATION

In an attempt to understand how plants and animals are related to one another, biologists have devised a scheme of classification for all living things. As with other groups of animals, bird species are divided into a hierarchy of groups, the broadest category of which is referred to as an order. The 134 or so species of owls that occur worldwide are placed in the order Strigiformes, within which there are two sub-groups called families. The family Tytonidae contains 10 species – the barn owls and close allies – represented in Britain by a single species. The remaining 124 species worldwide are placed in the Strigidae, and only four of these breed regularly in Britain: the tawny, little, long-eared and short-eared owls.

Shortly after they have fledged, young tawny owls can often be seen sitting in conspicuous sites in daylight. An adult will be near by.

Adaptations to a hunting life

With a diet restricted entirely to live prey, it is hardly surprising that owls are superbly adapted to a hunting lifestyle. In common with other avian predators such as falcons and eagles, they have beaks and talons ideally suited for the capture and killing of prey. However, unlike their diurnal counterparts most species of owls feed at night or in low light levels, and consequently their senses of vision and hearing are refined to suit their habits.

Small mammals such as voles and mice feature heavily in the diet of most species, including the barn owl.

LEISURELY WINGS

By the standards of most other birds, owls have wings with a surface area that is extremely large relative to their body weight. This allows them to fly at relatively low speeds in leisurely flight and glide with ease. Short-eared owls, for example, need only flap their wings twice per second, while at the other extreme many hummingbird species beat their wings 40–50 times per second. Characteristically, the wings of owls are broad and often rounded. They are proportionately longest in species such as barn owls which habitually quarter the ground (systematically flying up and down), or short-eared owls which regularly undertake long-distance flights. Shorter, rounder wings are seen in species such as little owls, as these typically feed by gliding short distances onto prey from elevated perches.

NIGHT VISION

Owl's eyes are without doubt their most striking feature, and they are also crucial to the birds' hunting skills. The ability of owls to see well enough in near darkness to feed and fly is firmly established in the minds of most people. The proportionately huge eyes with large pupils are obviously essential, and the retina at the back of each eye is packed with more low light-sensitive cells – known as rods – than most birds. The disadvantage of relying on rod cells is that they only allow owls to see in black and white. Although owl vision is demonstrably superb, detailed research reveals that the differences between owl vision and that of other animals are not as startling as was once supposed. For example, the sensitivity of many owl eyes to light is only about three times that of our own, although they are far more sensitive than the eyes of most diurnal birds.

PINPOINT HEARING

Long-eared and eagle owls are just two of many species worldwide which possess conspicuous ear-like feathers on their heads that can be raised and lowered at will. The association of these 'ear' tufts with the ears proper ends with the name, as the feathers have nothing whatsoever to do with hearing. The true ears of owls are concealed beneath the feathers of the head, and although hidden from view they are nevertheless crucial to the birds' ability to function after dark.

To enhance the pinpoint accuracy of their hearing, owls have evolved a number of special features. The external openings to the ears, which are sited on the margins of the

Despite outward appearances, the 'ear'-like tufts of feathers on this long-eared owl are designed for display rather than hearing. The true ears lie hidden by feathers on the lateral margins of the rounded facial disc.

SILENT FLIGHT

The leading edge of the tawny owl's primary feather shows adaptations for silent flight.

The element of surprise is important for many predators, owls not least among them. A refined sense of vision and hearing and an ability to fly at low speeds would count for little if prey became aware of the predator's presence prior to an attack. Hunting after dark dramatically reduces the chances of an owl being seen by small mammals, but there is still the problem of wing noise. Mice in particular have a notoriously good sense of hearing. Owls overcome this problem by having specially modified flight feathers that effectively muffle any sound they might otherwise make. The leading edge and the outer part of the trailing edge of these feathers are armed with stiffened barbs, while the upper surface is noticeably downy – these features serving to reduce airflow. Silent flight has another advantage for owls, enabling their sense of hearing (so important in hunting) to operate unimpaired by background noise.

facial disc, are asymmetrical both in terms of their size and their position. The stiff ruff of feathers that fringes the facial disc reflects sound towards the ears, thus increasing their sensitivity. Experiments clearly show that owl's hearing is an essential complement to its vision when it comes to its nocturnal lifestyle, its hunting in particular.

FIERCESOME FEET

Although not closely related to birds of prey, it is hardly surprising that owls have evolved a similar armoury of weapons to their day-flying equivalents for the capture and killing of prey. Their legs are both long and power-

Broad, rounded wings enable owls to fly amazingly slowly, and their flight pattern is leisurely and buoyant. For their size, owls are surprisingly light.

ful, with widely spreading feet armed with fiercely sharp talons. The undersurface of their feet is rough, which is no doubt an advantage when it comes to gripping prey. Victims such as small mammals are often killed by the initial impact of the feet and talons, but if a struggle ensues, the sharp, downcurved beak will quickly dispatch the prey. Food is occasionally torn up using the beak, particularly if the prey item is large or there are small owlets to be fed, but generally owls swallow most of their food whole.

Necks with an incredible degree of mobility allow owls to overcome the problem of eyes which are fixed in their sockets. They can rotate their heads through 360 degrees.

OWL EYES

Being scrutinised by the penetrating stare of an owl can be an unnerving experience. The disquieting effect of their gaze is at least partly because their eyes appear fixed and motionless, giving the impression that the bird is completely focused on the human observer, both mentally and visually. Unlike most other birds, the eyes of owls are indeed fixed in their sockets, and are forward-facing, framed by the large facial disc. Although this arrangement means that there is a large blind area behind the head, the advantage is a wide area of binocular vision in front of the eyes. Watch an owl for long enough and you will realise that the blind area does not really disadvantage the bird, as an extraordinarily flexible neck means that it can effectively rotate its head through 360 degrees.

A heart-shaped facial disc is typical of the barn owl and helps distinguish it from other species whose faces are rather rounded.

Large, fixed eyes can make the penetrating stare of an owl quite unnerving.

The diet of little owls is surprisingly varied and opportunistic. Earthworms and other invertebrates feature heavily, although small mammals and birds may sometimes be taken.

▶ *There are few more magnificent sights in the Arctic than a snowy owl in flight. During the long northern summers they have to hunt in daylight.*

◀ *Although many predators consider them distasteful, shrews frequently feature in the diet of barn owls – especially when there are several hungry mouths to feed back at the nest site.*

With their disproportionately large heads and bright eyes, owls have an appealing, almost cuddly appearance. This gentle exterior belies the truth, however, and in response to the tell-tale sight or sound of a small mammal, they reveal themselves as single-minded and successful killers.

FOOD AND FEEDING

Owls feed exclusively on animals, but unlike many day-flying birds of prey they seldom – if ever – take carrion. Despite the dramatic differences in size seen among owls as a group, the diet of a significant proportion of species worldwide, both large and small, comprises small mammals such as mice, rats and voles.

Much of the evidence for the diet of owls comes from analysing their regurgitated pellets, which contain the indigestible parts of their prey. The only problem with this approach is that prey animals that lack resistant components such as bones or wing cases often fail to be noticed, although with thorough and systematic investigation even the tiny bristles of earthworms can be detected. Although most owls take prey items that are comparatively small, some species are more ambitious. Eagle owls from Europe and great horned owls from North America, for example, routinely catch hares and rabbits and have been known to tackle prey the size of small deer.

Many owls are opportunistic feeders and the diet of any given species may vary throughout the year and across their range worldwide. Tawny owls are a case in point, as birds from rural woodland sites have a higher proportion of small mammals in their diet than their urban counterparts, who take considerable numbers of birds. Voles are a favourite food of short-eared owls, especially during the summer months, although ground-feeding birds become an important component of the diet in winter, especially in harsh weather. This particular owl species has a large geographical range and some of

the birds on the Galapagos Islands (600 miles off the coast of Ecuador) feed almost exclusively on storm-petrels for several months each year.

Invertebrates are another important and readily available source of food for many owls. Even species as large as the tawny owl

regularly take insects and earthworms, but the predominance of these creatures as prey is more apparent in the diet of small owls.

Perhaps the most unusual variations on the dietary theme are found in the fishing owls, a group comprising eight species throughout tropical Asia and Africa. As

OWL PELLETS

Although the nocturnal habits of most owls ensure that much of their behaviour passes unnoticed, the enterprising nature detective can often piece together clues about their diet. By swallowing most of their food whole, owls ensure that much of their prey remains intact. Following ingestion, the soft, fleshy parts of each animal are digested, leaving hard, indigestible elements such as bones and beetle wing cases to be discarded in the form of pellets.

Two pellets are generally regurgitated each day and these are coughed-up at regular roost sites. Even though the owl may change sites at regular intervals, the pellets often remain in one piece for a considerable period. To discover what an

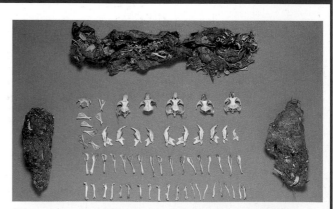

Dissecting owl pellets can provide valuable information about diet, as bones and skulls remain largely intact.

owl has eaten, place a pellet in water in a shallow tray. Gently tease it apart – don't worry, there is no smell associated with this process – to reveal the jaws and

skulls of small rodents and birds. Occasionally you might even come across a bird ring – make a note of the number and report it the British Trust for Ornithology.

their name suggests, they snatch fish from the surface of the water. Interestingly, these owls lack the flight feather adaptations that ensure silent flight in their more terrestrial counterparts.

CREATURES OF THE NIGHT?

More than half the world's owl species hunt after dark. Among the common British representatives of the group, the tawny and long-eared owls are essentially nocturnal, while the feeding periods of the remaining three species extend at least from dusk to dawn. Of this latter group, the short-eared owl is the most diurnal in its habits and is often seen flying in the middle of the day.

It comes as a surprise to some people to find that an impressive array of owl species breed in the Arctic regions of Europe, Asia and North America. Some, such as the snowy owl, favour areas of open tundra, while others, including hawk owls and great grey owls, are found at the northern limits of the tree zone. During the brief summer the sun

MIGRATION

In winter, the long-eared owl often takes short migrations to other areas for better feeding.

Migration between summer and winter quarters is a common phenomenon among many bird groups, and it is also seen in certain owl species. Cold, wintry weather inevitably has an impact on the availability and abundance of prey, and this has a knock-on effect upon those owls that depend on them. Particularly hard-hit are the owls which breed at northern latitudes. Short-eared owls routinely migrate south and west in autumn, and these continental birds arrive on Britain's east coast in October and November. Snowy owls are also affected in this way. Like other Arctic species such as the hawk owl, they are heavily influenced by population trends in lemmings, their usual prey. When numbers of these rodents crash, they are forced to move from their usual wintering grounds.

remains above the horizon and they have no choice but to hunt during the permanent daylight. During the winter however, when hours of daylight are limited, the birds will more regularly hunt at night.

HUNTING STRATEGIES

Broadly speaking, there are two main ways in which owls hunt. The one that arouses most interest among birdwatchers is the technique adopted by barn and short-eared owls – namely quartering low over grassy ground in slow, leisurely and buoyant flight. The response of these species to a tell-tale rustle in the vegetation below is immediate: the owl doubles back and plunges to the ground,

talons outstretched to grab the prey.

Most owls are territorial for at least part of the year and even those which disperse outside the breeding season soon come to know the terrain where they over-winter well. Crucial to the survival of these birds is a knowledge of suitable perches in any given habitat. From these vantage points, the owls survey the ground below, watching and listening out for indications of prey. Once a likely meal is located, the owl immediately glides down to the ground, again making its primary attack with its talons. This perch and pounce technique is clearly an effective one, as it is employed by most owl species in their overall pattern of hunting.

Seen briefly, a flying tawny owl can be confused with the barn owl, as the underwings look very pale.

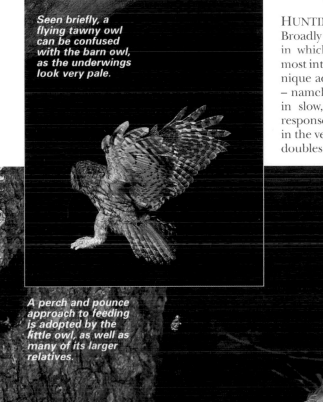

A perch and pounce approach to feeding is adopted by the little owl, as well as many of its larger relatives.

Although they will sometimes use a perch, barn owls typically quarter grassland in search of prey.

The arrival of spring heralds the onset of nesting for the breeding birds of Britain and Europe. In the case of songbirds, observers are left in little doubt as to the preoccupation of the birds in question, as the dawn chorus and displaying birds assault the ears and eyes of anyone venturing into the countryside. Although our owls are less demonstrative, nesting is still their primary concern at this time of year.

TERRITORY AND COURTSHIP

During the breeding season, all owls are distinctly territorial, the defended area comprising both the immediate vicinity of the nest itself and areas of good feeding. In migratory species, the behaviour lasts only as long as there are nests, eggs and young to defend, but with sedentary species, territoriality persists throughout the year.

Visual displays are clearly of limited use to those owl species that are entirely nocturnal. To make up for this, tawny owls, for example, are extremely vocal and are well known for the duetting 'tuwhit tuwhoo' calls uttered by pairs, and for a whole range of other vocalisations. These evocative sounds can be heard throughout the year, although the owls are particularly vocal in late winter and early spring. The range of calls uttered serve a variety of functions, including advertising the presence of birds in a territory to rivals, attracting mates for unpaired birds and reinforcing pair bonds in established pairs. Being at least partly diurnal, short-eared owls employ visual displays to advertise their presence in a territory, rival males establishing the boundaries of their domains in slow, wing-clapping displays.

Given the size and power of most owls and

the potential for inflicting damage on one another, it is not surprising that courtship is an essential precursor to mating, even in established pairs. Different species employ different techniques, but bobbing and swaying movements combined with ruffling of the feathers is common, as is the presentation of food by the male to the female.

NEST SITES

Comparatively few species of owl worldwide construct a nest of their own. Holes and recesses are favoured sites for many small- to medium-sized owls, while larger species may occupy the abandoned twiggy nests of crows or birds of prey. Some particularly large species, such as the snowy and eagle owls, will often just nest on the ground or on a rock ledge.

Hole-nesting species occupy a wide variety of sites, depending on the species. Tree holes are favoured by many, while ledges in man-made structures, such as farm buildings and warehouses, are often chosen by the aptly named barn owl. Some North American owls chose extraordinary nest sites. The tiny elf owl nests in saguaro cacti, using abandoned woodpecker nest holes, while burrowing owls favour the burrows of rabbits and prairie dogs.

Short-eared owls are ground-nesters, often using clumps of heather or grass to provide a degree of shelter. Infant conifer plantations are often favoured in upland areas of Britain.

Tree cavities are a favoured nest site for the tawny owl, our most common and widespread woodland species. Adults vigorously defend the young against intruders.

Depending on the species and the particular season, most owls lay between two and 10 eggs, the usual clutch being three or four. In all cases, the eggs are rounded and white. Conventional wisdom attributes their colour – atypical among birds as a whole – to the fact that, being mainly hole nesters, cryptic markings or colours would serve no purpose.

Young owls are an endearing sight once they have acquired the downy covering of feathers so characteristic at this stage in their lives. Some of the downy feathers persist even after the young fledge and leave the nest, making it easy to tell them from their parents, which often remain in attendance for some time.

ROAD KILLS

A sad indictment of modern times is that most people are more familiar with owls as road casualties than as living birds. Many thousands of owls are killed by traffic each year – barn, tawny and little owls in particular – the birds often being lured to roadside verges by the prospect of hunting for small mammals. Short of removing the vegetation from beside our roads, it is difficult to see what can be done to reduce this annual carnage.

Brilliant orange eyes make long-eared owlets particularly appealing.

There are few more comical sights in the animal world than a brood of young barn owls quizzically scrutinising a visitor to their nest site.

The snowy owl makes its nest on the ground. Given the often frozen nature of the ground in its Arctic environment, the eggs need constant incubation from the brooding female.

OWL BOXES

A number of positive, practical measures can be undertaken to help with the conservation of owls. Chief among these is the placement of artificial nest boxes in suitable locations. Tawny owls will readily take to large, open-fronted boxes if these are firmly attached to the side branches of tall trees and

One of the more positive discoveries of recent years is the willingness of barn owls to take to artificial nest boxes. This has helped greatly with the species' conservation.

placed well out of reach of children. Little owls also favour this type of box but, on account of their smaller size, they will occupy smaller boxes placed nearer to the ground.

Barn owls also respond well to nesting schemes, often using a strengthened, flat shelf in the eaves of a barn. A prime consideration in the placement of the shelf must be that the owls should not be disturbed by the sight of human activities while sitting on the nest.

Barn owl – silent white hunter

Otherwise known as the screech owl, and even 'death's dreadful messenger', the barn owl has an undeservedly macabre reputation. In fact, for centuries it was the farmers' best friend, welcomed into barns for its great rat-hunting abilities.

THE BARN OWL IS THE MOST international of the owls – indeed the most widely distributed land bird in the world, found in every continent except Antarctica. The northernmost members of its far flung family are the barn owls of Scotland. The white-breasted form familiar in Britain is found in the southern and western parts of Europe, while the brown-breasted form – which is better suited to colder climates – is dominant to the north and east. Over the entire range, there are some 35 subspecies.

Barn owls are strikingly handsome birds, with pronounced facial discs and relatively small, dark eyes compared with most other owls. Flying overhead they appear almost completely white because of their white breasts; the plumage of their heads and backs is golden-buff. They have an extensive repertoire of extraordinary sounds – screams, squeaks, chirrups and snores – each with its own particular function. The screech is the male's courtship song, which he uses to attract a mate or to announce his occupation of the territory. The female owl responds with a similar screech when she and the male are engaged in courtship flight. Another extraordinary sound is the 'snoring' emitted by a brood of hungry owlets when they want their parents to bring food. This sound is also used during courtship by the adult female, calling on the male to feed her. This 'snoring' sounds so strange that it often becomes the subject of letters to the press from folk who just can't believe that it's a chorus of fluffy owlets!

Traditionally, the barn owl was thought to

A fluffy barn owl chick may be small and helpless, but when it's hungry it produces an extraordinary 'snoring' sound that has to be heard to be believed!

owe its hunting success to its remarkable powers of vision. Certainly in adequate light conditions its eyesight is excellent. Like other owls, and ourselves, it has binocular vision which enables it to locate its prey with extreme accuracy. It also has the amazing ability to turn its head so far round that it can cover a field of 360 degrees (quite disconcerting for the observer) and look directly upwards as well.

In poor light conditions the barn owl's vision is not as good as that of the tawny or the long-eared owl. However, this is more

GHOST OWL

Of all the owls, the barn owl has the most sinister reputation – it has been widely regarded as a bird of ill omen, presaging doom and disaster. Until recently, many people in Britain believed that an owl screeching on their roof was a warning of an imminent death in the family. In some areas the owl's shriek foretold a birth, or that a girl was about to lose her virginity.

So how did the barn owl get such a spooky reputation? It must be due, at least in part, to its ghostly appearance and habits. The sight of this silent white hunter haunting the moonlit skies around ruins and churchyards is spine-chilling enough, but combined with the owl's blood-curdling call (which earned it the country name of 'scritch' or 'screech' owl) it's not hard to see why it was associated with the souls of the dead.

One of the eeriest stories about barn owls actually seems to be true. Well-substantiated accounts of owls that glowed in the dark are believed to be the result of birds roosting on decayed wood and getting their plumage impregnated with luminous bacteria.

Believe it or not, an average sized family of barn owls can take well over 1,000 rodents in a year – no wonder farmers used to welcome them into their barns.

BARN OWL FACT FILE

Most often encountered as a ghostly white image in the night, the barn owl is unmistakable. The bird appears exceptionally pale from the underside, its strong wings with soft-edged feathers aiding its noiseless flight. The barn owl has declined considerably over the last half century, but farmers who are aware of this beautiful bird's needs can still provide a suitable habitat with sensitive land management.

● **NAMES**
English name: Barn owl
Scientific name: *Tyto alba*

● **SIZE**
33–35 cm;
male 280–315 g,
female 310–350 g

● **KEY FEATURES**
White, heart-shaped face with black eyes; mostly white body; head, back and upperside of wings golden-buff with some grey; females generally more silver grey than males, with black or grey spots on underside

● **NEST**
Eggs laid in a depression in pellet debris in tree holes, buildings and nest-boxes

● **BREEDING**
Eggs laid in April or May; not unusual to have 2 broods

● **EGGS**
4–6 eggs, chalky white; laid at intervals of 2–3 days; incubation 30–31 days

● **YOUNG**
Fledge after 55–65 days; naked first then soft covering of down

● **FOOD**
Small mammals: voles, mice, shrews; quarters fields, hunts from perches

● **VOICE**
Screeching calls; young have a loud hissing/snoring call

● **HABITAT**
Open lowlands, rough grassland, herbage, hedges, banks, ditches and roadside verges

● **FLIGHT TIMES**
Just before sunset until dawn

Distribution Map Key

■ Present all year round
■ Present during summer months
■ Present during winter months
☐ Not present

BARN OWLS IN THE BRITISH ISLES

● **DISTRIBUTION**
Lowland areas, predominantly farmland, below 300 m; uncommon, estimated 5,000 pairs in Britain and Ireland in 1985; decline due to agricultural practices and 3–5,000 road deaths per year

● **STATUS**
Scarce in most areas

Asymmetrical ears enable the barn owl to pinpoint the direction of sounds with precision.

The stiff feathers of the facial disc funnel sounds to the bird's sensitive ears, which are protected by adjustable ear flaps.

Although the owl looks large, it has a small body beneath deep, soft feathering.

The long, closely feathered legs enable it to reach down into the tall vegetation and seize its prey.

The owl's fiercely-taloned feet are its principal hunting weapons. The outer toe on each foot is reversible to aid the capture of its prey and to enable the owl to keep a firm grip on it in flight. Tiny scales on the pads of its feet help it to maintain its grip on a struggling animal.

The serrated leading edge to the wing breaks up the wind-flow and aids silent flight.

PROTECTED!

The barn owl is afforded special protection under Schedule One of the Wildlife and Countryside Act, 1981. It is an offence to disturb them at the nest without a licence.

Hunting by hearing

For the barn owl, silent flight and acute hearing are vital to its hunting technique. Pinpointing its prey after a deliberate search, the hunt ends in a dramatic swoop.

Large, rounded wings give the barn owl the power and manoeuvrability to patrol slowly and intently over field edges and grassland, often hovering low above the ground.

1 & 2 Patrolling from the air, the owl systematically quarters its hunting territory. Barn owls are birds of the open countryside: they hunt over rough grassland, in weedy corners and along hedgerows and ditches.

3 Listening hard as it flies silently along, the owl's kee[n] hearing picks up the rustlin[g] sound of a vole moving ab[ove] far below.

As the owl uses its wings to slow down for a night kill, it swings its feet to and fro before making a final grab for its prey.

than compensated for by its remarkable hearing. Experiments have shown that the barn owl can identify and locate its prey in complete darkness, solely by sound. The ear openings are protected by adjustable ear flaps and one is slightly higher than the other, enabling the owl to judge the source of rustles and squeaks on the ground with a high degree of accuracy.

DISCOVERING THE BARN OWL'S DIET

So what does the barn owl's prey consist of? You can find out what they have eaten fairly accurately by examining the pellets of undigested food they regurgitate. As an owl's digestive system has difficulty dealing with bones, particularly the skulls of small animals, these pellets give us a pretty good picture of its diet. The thumb-sized pellets are distinctive – black with a varnished-looking surface. The owl usually casts about two a day, and these accumulate at regular breeding and roosting sites, some of which have been occupied for more than 100 years.

Using this evidence, it has been shown that up to 95 per cent of the barn owl's diet consists of small mammals – shrews, voles, mice and rats. These are either caught as it patrols its regular route along field borders and roadside verges, or when it drops down from a watchful perch on a fence post. The remainder of its prey comprises small birds, snatched from bushes as it flies past, along with a small number of bats, moles, lizards and amphibians. The owl doesn't seem to seek out particular animals, instead it takes what is available, though it may opt for larger prey when it has a family of chicks to feed.

Barn owls typically roost and rest in sites close to humans. These may be natural sites such as holes in trees, or man-made ones such as barns, churches, ruins and quarries. Traditional farm buildings often include

'owl holes' – entrances constructed to allow barn owls to rest on the rafters in the roof space – as farmers wisely welcomed their contribution to vermin control around the farm. In recent years the felling of hollow trees and the conversion of barns to country residences have seriously reduced potential homes for barn owls. Happily, this shortage is being partly offset by the erection of custom-built nest boxes, which many owls seem willing to accept.

Many barn owls remain on their territory throughout the winter, paired with the same mate. As early as February the pair renew their bond by preening each other and by screeching and chasing around their territory. The female starts calling to the mate with snoring sounds, like an owlet begging for food. He responds by bringing food and copulation follows, often repeated every few minutes.

Barn owls have a long breeding season, the longest of any owl. In the main part of their range, where prey is abundant, they may breed throughout the year. In Britain

they start laying as early as February and will continue until October, with the peak season running from April to July. Most other British owls produce only a single brood, with many late families being replacement broods or the result of late pairings.

The barn owl doesn't make a nest as such, but the place where the eggs will be laid (which is usually chosen from the roosting area) soon becomes lined with pellets and debris. The eggs are matt white in colour and elliptical in shape, whereas most owl eggs are round. The clutch usually numbers between four and seven, though there may be up to 13 eggs in years when prey is abundant, laid at intervals of about two days.

Young owls can be heard calling inside the eggs shortly before hatching. A tiny hole appears in a shell one evening, and the mother breaks off chips of the eggshell with

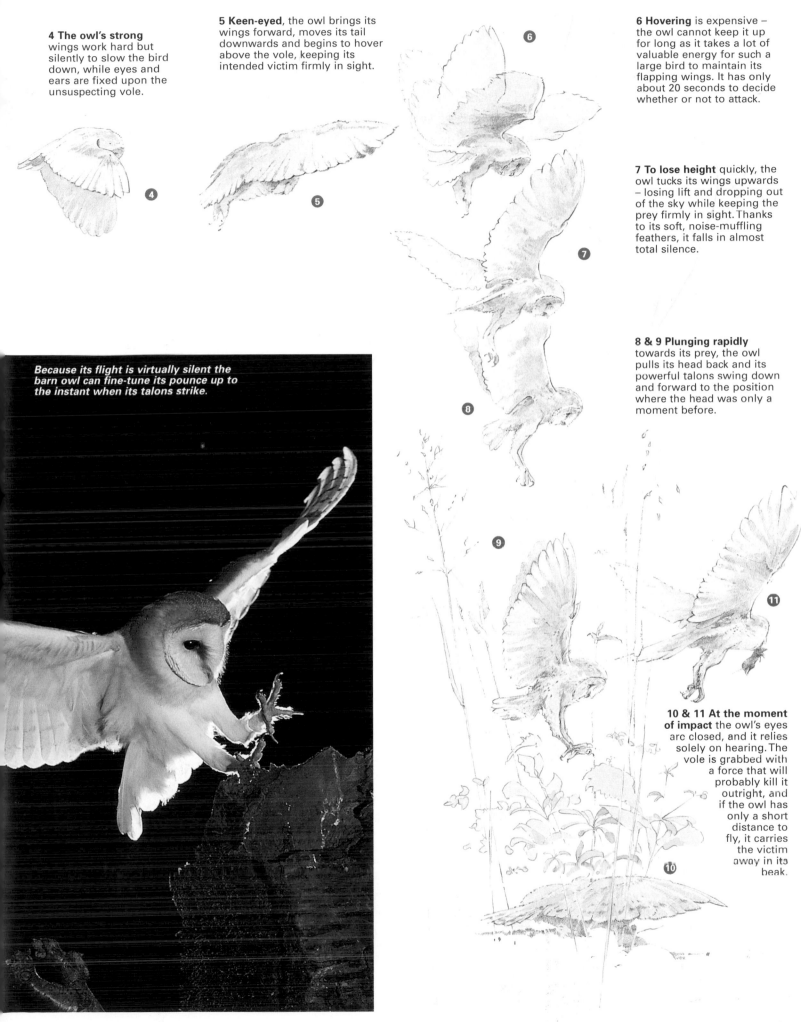

4 The owl's strong wings work hard but silently to slow the bird down, while eyes and ears are fixed upon the unsuspecting vole.

5 Keen-eyed, the owl brings its wings forward, moves its tail downwards and begins to hover above the vole, keeping its intended victim firmly in sight.

6 Hovering is expensive – the owl cannot keep it up for long as it takes a lot of valuable energy for such a large bird to maintain its flapping wings. It has only about 20 seconds to decide whether or not to attack.

7 To lose height quickly, the owl tucks its wings upwards – losing lift and dropping out of the sky while keeping the prey firmly in sight. Thanks to its soft, noise-muffling feathers, it falls in almost total silence.

8 & 9 Plunging rapidly towards its prey, the owl pulls its head back and its powerful talons swing down and forward to the position where the head was only a moment before.

Because its flight is virtually silent the barn owl can fine-tune its pounce up to the instant when its talons strike.

10 & 11 At the moment of impact the owl's eyes are closed, and it relies solely on hearing. The vole is grabbed with a force that will probably kill it outright, and if the owl has only a short distance to fly, it carries the victim away in its beak.

17

her beak to help the chick emerge the following day. At first the youngster will be covered with sparse white down, which is replaced by longer, thicker, creamy white down over the first fortnight. As two or three days may elapse between the hatching of consecutive chicks, a brood of barn owlets is a strangely mixed bunch, and the first one can be 30 days older than the youngest. This staggered hatching is a strategy for dealing with a variable food supply. The largest chick gets fed first, then the second, and so on. Thus, when food is short, the youngest chicks may starve, but at least some of the brood survive.

ARE WE LOSING THE BARN OWL?

The British barn owl population has been subject to a gradual but steady decline for a century. There have been similar declines in other European countries, and also in the United States. So what are the reasons for the reduction in numbers of this splendid bird, particularly in Britain?

The answer may well be in the way owls survive the winter. Barn owls differ from the other owls of temperate regions in one important way: most such owls – the tawny owl for example – put on weight in winter to maintain warmth and provide reserves for the period when food is hard to find. Barn owls on the other hand, have a lower body weight in winter than in spring and summer, and seem unable to build up reserves. This may be because owls in tropical and sub-tropical zones (where the barn owl is thought to have originated) have little need of fat reserves to tide them over, but in northerly areas the species is more vulnerable to food shortage and severe weather. The female is under special stress at this time as she is at

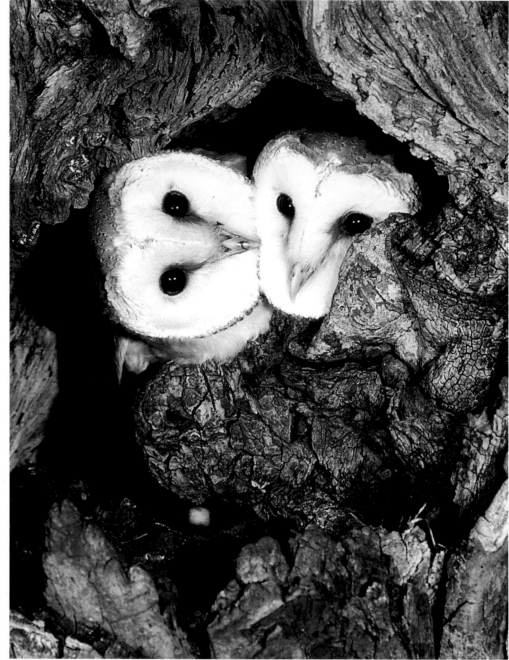

► *A hollow tree is a favourite barn owl nesting site when they can find one, but felling of hollow trees has made it a rare treat.*

▼ *If disturbed at the nest, the adult barn owl adopts a defensive pose, sheltering the young owlets behind its wings.*

her lowest weight in late winter and early spring – just when she needs to build up her body reserves in readiness for breeding.

As well as this natural vulnerability, several other factors also affect British barn owls, some natural and some man-made. Natural factors include the incidence of severe winters and prolonged periods of wet weather, which make it much harder for the owl to find food; plus the three to four year population cycle of voles – the barn owl's principal prey. Barn owl numbers might be expected to recover from such events in otherwise favourable circumstances, but the use of toxic chemicals on farmland had severe effects on barn owls in the late 1950s and early 1960s, especially in the east of England. Loss of suitable nest sites in some areas also influenced populations. Overall, modern methods of agriculture must be one of the most important factors in the decline of the barn owl, as they reduce the amount of suitable habitat available.

THE BARN OWL CALENDAR

JANUARY • FEBRUARY

A difficult time. Numbers of small mammals have declined since the end of the owls' breeding season, making it more difficult to locate enough food. Poor weather can also have a disastrous effect on their ability to hunt. It is the time of the highest natural mortality.

MARCH • APRIL

If we have a mild winter, the owls will be in better condition and will begin nesting in March. Poor weather can put it back well into April. The nest could be a floor, ledge, tree hole or even a beam in a building. Loss of nesting sites is a major problem, although nest-boxes can provide suitable alternatives.

MAY • JUNE

Most females will be incubating their eggs during this period, briefly leaving the nest two or three times a day for a stretch and to relieve themselves. The male will provide all sustenance for the pair. When the young hatch, the male will have to provide an increased amount of food.

JULY • AUGUST

Chicks will be growing well now. Once they have a covering of down, the female will help with the hunting. If there is a shortage of available prey the youngest chicks may starve as their older and larger siblings monopolise the food supply.

SEPTEMBER • OCTOBER

All the young should have left the nest by now and will be wandering in search of their own territories. Studies show that most young owls remain fairly close to their parents' territory, but it is during this period that owls may be seen in unexpected locations.

NOVEMBER • DECEMBER

Life again becomes difficult as prey numbers decline and the weather worsens. The young will have been on individual territories for some time now. It is unusual to see even the adults at the previous summer's nest site.

WILDLIFE WATCH

WHERE CAN I SEE BARN OWLS IN THE WILD?

● If you're lucky enough to have a garden that backs on to fields or a river, you may have the chance to spot an owl very close to home. Quiet and patient waiting, with a pair of binoculars if you have them, may reward you with a sighting of a barn owl.

● Good places to look for barn owls are water meadows, field edges, rough grassland by rivers, streams, ditches, hedgerows, lakes, roadside verges and set-aside land.

● You have the chance to spot a barn owl all year round as it is a resident species in the British Isles. The best times of day to see one are just after sunset and just before dawn, but barn owls can be seen any time of night and occasionally during the day.

WHERE CAN I SEE CAPTIVE BARN OWLS?

● Visiting an owl sanctuary is a good way to help owls directly, to learn more about them and also – of course – to guarantee that you will actually see some of these beautiful creatures close up.

● Most zoos will have an owl exhibit, and wildlife rescue centres will often have barn owls – some of which will be rehabilitated and released, while others may be too badly injured to cope in the wild.

● A good starting point for a barn owl search in the north of England is the headquarters of the World Owl Trust at The Owl Centre in Ravenglass, Cumbria, Tel: (01229) 717393.
 If you live further south, try the New Forest Owl Sanctuary at Crow, near Ringwood in Hampshire, Tel: (01425) 476487.

Tawny owl – a real night owl

The tawny owl is typical of everything that comes to mind when we think about owls – it is nocturnal, goes '*tuwhit tuwhoo*', has big eyes and eats small mammals. The tawny is also common and widespread, even in city gardens and parks.

IT MAY SEEM ALL TOO OBVIOUS TO say that the tawny owl is active at night – after all, that's more or less the definition of an owl isn't it? However this is only true up to a point, as some owls are more nocturnal than others. The little owl can often be seen out hunting in daylight for example; the tawny owl on the other hand, is the most nocturnal of our British birds.

During the day a tawny owl doses quietly, tucked up against a tree trunk where it passes unnoticed. At night, eyes wide open, it sits on a convenient perch and scans the ground below. It is waiting for an unwary small mammal to venture into the open – the owl's next meal.

AN OWL'S EYE

The eyes of a tawny owl are almost as large as those of a human. They are almost tubular rather than spherical, and so big that they cannot swivel in their sockets – instead the owl turns its whole head to look in a different direction.

Each eye is incredibly sensitive to light and movement. The owl can see things in the dark when we cannot see at all, and their night vision is between 50 and 100 times more sensitive than our own. They are able to see a mouse when it is illuminated by the equivalent of a candle held several hundred metres away.

Throughout most of its range, including Britain, the tawny hunts almost exclusively by night. However, in northern parts of Europe, summer nights are short (only about four hours in Finland, for example), so tawnies can be seen hunting in daylight morning hours. The other exception to the 'night hunting rule' is when the owls have a brood of hungry owlets to feed. At these times they may hunt later in the morning and earlier in the evening than they otherwise would.

So where do tawny owls spend their days, and why do we seldom see them? After all, they are the commonest British owl and are widely distributed through the mainland. The truth is that the tawny owl is so splendidly camouflaged that it is far from easy to see, particularly in its favourite habitat – broad-leaved woodlands, wooded parks and gardens.

OUR INVISIBLE NEIGHBOUR

With its large round head, huge eyes and short body, the tawny is most people's idea of what an owl should look like – with a conspicuous and easily recognised silhouette. However, the plumage of British tawnies is a rich chestnut brown, beautifully streaked and speckled, and an excellent disguise in dappled woodland light. So when the owl is perched motionless on a branch, sitting close to the tree trunk with its silhouette concealed, it's no wonder it can spend most of its days dozing peacefully.

The tawny is often 'heard but not seen' (to reverse the usual phrase). It is a remarkably vocal bird, and has an amazing range of songs and calls. Of the sounds made by adults in the breeding season, ten different calls have been identified, plus five calls made by the young.

The most famous of the tawny calls, usually written as '*tuwhit tuwhoo*' (by Shakespeare among others), is really two calls and is be made by two birds. The '*kewick*' ('*tuwhit*') is a contact call, most often made by the female, though the male uses it too. The hoot ('*tuwhoo*') is the male's song, made both as a courtship and a territorial call, and when the male is bringing food for the female. During courtship the female may answer '*kewick*' to the male's '*hooo*', hence the '*tuwhit tuwhoo*' – but as a duet not a solo. Tawny owls call throughout the year, more during some seasons than others. They call less when the weather is cold, wet or windy, and at full moon. They also call in daylight hours.

The tawny is a versatile hunter and uses an extensive repertoire of hunting strategies to catch a wide range of mammals. Its principal

TAWNY OWL FACT FILE

The tawny is Britain's most numerous owl, with about 20,000 pairs breeding here. It is widespread in woodlands, farmland and even built-up areas throughout the British mainland, yet it is absent from Ireland, the Isle of Man and even the Isle of Wight, being clearly reluctant to fly over water. Tawny owls are probably decreasing in numbers.

Tawny owls come in two colour forms, the rich chestnut brown familiar in Britain, and a grey form we seldom see here.

● **NAMES**
English name: Tawny owl
Latin name: *Strix aluco*

● **SIZE**
Grows to 38 cm;
350–500 g

● **KEY FEATURES**
Large head, stout body, streaked chestnut brown plumage, black eyes

● **NEST**
Holes in trees, old nests of large birds, squirrel dreys, old buildings and holes in the ground; readily accepts nestboxes; nests are shallow, unlined hollows

● **EGGS**
2–4 white eggs, nearly round, laid at intervals; incubated by the female; hatch in approx. 4 weeks

● **FOOD**
Varied; chiefly small rodents, birds and insects

● **VOICE**
Hoot (male), '*kewick*' both sexes, plus a range of other calls; very vocal

● **BREEDING**
Mid-March (though sometimes a month earlier) to mid-June; single-brooded

● **YOUNG**
Nestling covered with white down; fledge between 28–37 days, but depend on parents for food for up to 3 months after leaving nest

● **FLIGHT TIMES**
Most nocturnal owl

● **HABITAT**
Deciduous woodland, parks with trees, large gardens

● **DISTRIBUTION**
Widespread throughout England, Wales and Scotland; not found in Ireland, Scottish Isles or Isle of Man

● **STATUS**
The commonest British owl

Distribution Map Key

■ Present all year round

□ Present during summer months

▨ Present during winter months

□ Not present

TAWNY OWLS IN THE BRITISH ISLES

Dagger-sharp talons on each foot hold prey in a lethal grip. As the toes close, the hind claw pierces the prey and ensures its rapid death. The owl's legs and toes are feathered, providing some protection from the bites of mice and rats.

The streaky brown plumage of a tawny owl makes it hard to see, except when it perches out in the open. Normally it is well camouflaged against tree bark, especially in the gloomy light of the forest.

How the tawny owl hunts

Typically, the tawny owl is an ambush predator. It sits motionless on a perch waiting to pounce on small mammals below. Flying about in dense woodland is difficult anyway, and wastes energy. When the owl does strike, it is silent and deadly.

1 The tawny is a night hunter. Selecting a suitable vantage point, it waits, watches and listens for a small animal on the forest floor, before launching itself towards its prey.

With perfect judgement and silent wingbeats, the tawny owl flies in to perch on a branch. Its broad wings allow slow flight, necessary in the cramped spaces among the branches of woodland trees.

2 On silent wings, the owl drops swiftly down from above. The chosen victim has little warning of the owl's sudden approach.

The main prey items are voles and other small woodland mammals. However, the tawny often takes small rabbits, moles and considerable numbers of earthworms.

3 At the last moment the owl spreads its wings over the prey and kills it swiftly with its powerful talons.

prey are the voles of its forest home, along with mice and shrews. Sitting quietly on a perch, it watches and listens to everything that goes on, then swiftly drops down and seizes the prey in its talons, killing it immediately. It also hunts on the wing, snatching birds from their roosts and sometimes beating bushes to startle small birds into flight. The tawny will even seize incubating birds the size of blackbirds off the nest. Insects such as beetles also form a substantial part of its diet, as do numbers of earthworms and molluscs. If standing water is available, water shrews and frogs will be on the menu too.

NIGHT VISION

The pellets of a tawny owl are of a similar size to the barn owl's, but they look quite different. They are grey and loose in texture, whereas the barn owl has black, compact pellets with a varnished appearance. However when the tawny has been eating mainly insects and earthworms, its pellets look rather different – small, brown, and packed with beetle wing cases, earthworm bristles and earth and plant material.

Hearing and vision, the senses needed for hunting, are both good in the tawny owl. The threshold of its visual activity is higher than most other nocturnal animals, while its daytime vision is similar to that of a pigeon, which is only active by day (though it cannot see as well as humans). The tawny's large external ear openings enable the owl to hear low and medium frequencies about 10

MOBBING PARTIES

Sometimes parties of small birds discover the tawny owl in its daytime roost and attack it with much calling and commotion. Tits, robins, blackbirds, thrushes, and jays are active in these 'mobbing' parties, all birds which the tawny preys on during its night-time forays. They crowd closer and closer to the owl, sneaking in and flicking it with their wings as if daring it to respond.

The calls used by mobbing birds are special ones, understood by all species. These alert birds in the neighbourhood to the presence of a predator and call them to help drive it away. Blackbirds use a loud *'chink chinking'* call and jays even seem to imitate the hoot of the owl, as if to identify the predator.

Sometimes the owl tries to fly away to escape its attackers, which follow it with even noisier alarm calls. But if, as usually happens, the owl remains motionless on its patch, the angry birds get tired and eventually leave it alone.

Owls throughout the world are mobbed by songbirds, but in Britain the tawny is particularly the subject of attack. Small birds are alert to the general shape of the owl, even when it is hardly visible to the human eye. Over centuries hunters have used decoys to catch birds for the pot – sticky bird lime is smeared on the twigs round the tethered owl, so that when birds come in to mob it they are caught and slaughtered. Sadly, this practice still continues in some parts of the world.

Tawny owls rarely sit out in the open during the day, as small birds will mob the owl if they spot it, making an awful fuss and noise.

times better than we do, although its upper frequency limit is probably similar to our own. Probably the tawny owl's most remarkable feature is its excellent memory. Experiments have shown it to be far better than a selection of other birds, and also cats and dogs – a valuable tool for a hunter.

Tawny owls pair for life and may be seen together all year round – perhaps perched on the same tree. They remain in their territory throughout the year, often for many years in succession. Their 'breeding year' starts in October or November, when established owls confirm ownership of their territory. Young owls born earlier in the year will now be sexually mature and ready to breed. They must first lay claim to a territory – perhaps inside that of their parents. This is crucial to their lives, because if they fail, they are likely to starve.

Initially boundary disputes are highly aggressive, accompanied by a great deal of hooting and calling. The male tawny owl establishes the territorial boundaries and the female selects the nest hole. Gradually the pairs settle down and start to roost together. Towards the end of the year, the male tawny starts to bring food to his mate – 'courtship feeding' as it is called. This not only confirms their partnership, but enables the female to build up reserves ready for breeding. During courtship the male will also chase the female round and round the territory, making an extraordinary selection of screeching noises. Once paired, tawny owls are normally faithful to the same partner – although some male tawnies have been known to pair with more than one female.

Tawny owls are not only aggressive in defence of their territories but also their young – the female particularly. Mothers have been known to attack a person approaching the nest, even to the point of drawing blood with their talons. Two such incidents in Britain have resulted in the victim losing an eye. One of these was Eric Hosking, the famous bird photographer. This extreme aggression is unusual however, and seems most likely to occur in areas where there is a lot of human disturbance.

SETTING UP HOME

The tawny owl's traditional nest site is a natural hole in a tree, but they will also nest in chimneys, ruins, old nests made by other birds (crows, magpies and buzzards), and even in squirrels' dreys. In areas where there are few mature trees, such as in southwest Scotland, tawnies also nest on the ground. One resourceful pair even set up home under the back seat of an old Morris car abandoned on a rubbish tip!

Tawnies' eggs are typical owl eggs – white and round. They are laid early, in March, so that the parents can catch enough small mammals for their chicks before the undergrowth shoots up and hides them. There is usually an interval of three to four days between the laying of the first and second eggs, otherwise the interval is 48 hours. Two to four eggs will be laid in all, and these are incubated by the female alone. It seems that incubation doesn't start until the second egg is laid, and indeed the first egg is by no means always the first to hatch.

After hatching the male bird brings more food for the young. The female does not leave the nest until the chicks are six to seven days old, when she may leave briefly to go hunting. Otherwise she remains nearby. Young tawny

Tawny owls like to nest in hollow trees, which is why they are often found in woodland or farmland where old trees are available. In young plantations there are few hollows and the owls will use the substitutes provided – in the form of large, tunnel-like nest boxes.

WILDLIFE WATCH

WHERE TO LOOK FOR TAWNY OWLS

● Tawny owls are noisy birds, especially in the winter months. Their calls will indicate where to look for them at dusk, and there is no substitute for patient waiting until one comes into sight. During the day, the owl's position is most likely to be given away by the alarm calls of small birds when it is being mobbed. It is always worth investigating to find out what is going on, and you may be lucky enough to see the owl.

● In urban areas, tawny owls are often easier to see than in the countryside. This is because they have fewer places to hide and also because the city night is never really dark. Street lamps provide sufficient light for you to spot the owls, even late at night. Often they sit on television aerials or chimneys, right out in the open.

BEST LEFT ALONE

Tawny owls leave the nest at about five weeks old, long before they are able to look after themselves. At first they remain in the vicinity and their parents return to feed them. The young make special calls to ensure the adults can find them, and so that the brood doesn't get mixed up with any other young tawny families. Young owls depend on their parents for food for up to three months after they leave the nest, and during this time they gradually learn to fend for themselves and to establish territories of their own.

At this stage of their lives, owlets are often discovered by well-meaning people who think that the youngsters have lost their parents or been abandoned. The adults will almost certainly be close by and will return to care for them. A hand-reared owl which hasn't been taught to hunt by its parents will only starve when released into the wild.

The eggs are incubated by the female. She is very protective of her family and will fiercely attack intruders. She can inflict very serious wounds with her sharp talons.

The young tawny owlets will continue to be fed by their parents for several weeks after leaving the nest. They can often be found out in the open.

owls depend on their parents for food for up to three months after leaving the nest, and it is at this time – while they are learning to fend for themselves – that there is a very high rate of mortality among the young owls.

The tawny owl is the commonest and most widespread owl in Europe and also in Britain. In Britain it is found almost throughout mainland England, Wales, and Scotland, although it is less frequent in the more northerly parts of Scotland. It has not made its way to Ireland however, or to the islands such as the Isle of Man, or those off the coast of Scotland. The tawny owl is not an apt coloniser.

During the 19th century, tawny numbers decreased significantly – a decrease attributed to persecution by game keepers, as tawnies were thought to be affecting the availability of young rabbits and hares, more highly valued than today. From 1900 to 1930 numbers started to rise, especially after the decline in keepering during world war I. In some areas this increase continued until the 1950s. Since then, tawny numbers have remained largely stable, apart from some minor fluctuations caused by the cycles of rodent populations, severe winters and the use of organochlorine pesticides.

So what is the secret of the tawny owl's success, compared for example with the barn owl? It is a very versatile bird, and its repertoire of hunting techniques enable it to take a wide range of prey – thus it is not affected by the scarcity of a preferred species. Again, unlike the barn owl, tawnies build up their fat reserves before the onset of winter. Not only does this aid the owl's chances of survival, but it also leaves the female in better condition at the start of the breeding season.

The tawny owl has not only maintained, but also extended the range of habitats in which it lives. It has become 'the' garden owl, and has spread through suburbs and parks in the centre of cities. Its readiness to accept nestboxes has enabled it to move into new habitats such as the large areas of mature conifer plantation now found in several parts of the country. For the moment, the tawny owl population looks secure.

The baby owls soon grow a thick covering of fluffy down, making them look like soft toys. Nevertheless, they are quite fierce and will hiss and snap their beaks sharply if disturbed.

Both parents care for the young. The female remains close to her chicks, especially for the first few days after hatching. The male works overtime to catch additional prey to feed his family.

The young can fly when they are about five weeks old. At this stage, they still retain much of their fluffy down. This is gradually replaced by normal feathers, often more greyish than in the adult.

25

Little owl – the owl that came to stay

The little owl is the only resident owl deliberately introduced into this country, yet today it is probably the second commonest British owl. Long ago it was associated with Athene, the Greek goddess of wisdom.

Occasionally during courtship the male little owl hovers above a sitting female or they may pursue one another in flight.

TWO HUNDRED YEARS ago, we would not have found the little owl throughout much of England and Wales as we do today. We might have seen the occasional bird that had been deliberately released into the wild, but at that time they didn't become established here.

As the 19th century progressed, introducing little owls became quite a popular pastime. It wasn't too hard to get hold of the birds for release, as animal dealers regularly brought them across the Channel for sale as household pets. Apparently they were champion cockroach killers! Little owls were set free in Yorkshire, Hertfordshire and Hampshire, then in Northamptonshire and Kent. These last two efforts finally seem to have led to the owls becoming breeding residents.

The first nest was seen in Northamptonshire in 1889, and after this the little owls spread rapidly. By 1920 they had reached every English county south of the Humber, and much of Wales too. In 1958 they bred in Scotland for the first time, though they have not spread beyond the southern counties and have yet to breed in Ireland. In recent years, their numbers have declined in some areas but increased in others. On the whole their population seems reasonably stable.

FUNNY LITTLE OWL

Little owls are rather comical characters, which is possibly why they became so popular as pets. When relaxed, perched on a post perhaps, the owl looks round and dumpy. But when alarmed or curious it stretches up on its long legs, looking tall and thin, and stares with its typical 'frowning' expression. Occasionally it decides to get a better view of something by turning its head upside down, which can be quite disconcerting to watch.

The little owl is not as strictly nocturnal as some other owls, so may be spotted sitting in a tree or on a post during daylight hours. Males begin to set up territories during February and call from a favourite perch to advertise their territory.

LITTLE OWL FACT FILE

This is Britain's smallest owl, often seen perched on fence posts in broad daylight. Its bright staring eyes give the bird a wild look compared to the more gentle appearance of the tawny owl. Of all the British owls it is the most likely to be seen by day, although it is rare in most of Scotland. It feeds mainly on large insects.

The prominent white eyebrows and flattish head are characteristic of this species.

- **NAMES**
English name: Little owl
Scientific name: *Athene noctua*

- **SIZE**
22 cm;
140–225 g

- **KEY FEATURES**
Small and squat with long legs, brown and white mottled plumage, golden eyes and pale 'eyebrows'; active by day; bobs up and down if alarmed or curious

- **NEST**
Holes in trees, ruins, cliffs, burrows; will use nest boxes; no nest – scrape in debris

- **BREEDING**
April–May; single brooded

- **EGGS**
3–5 eggs, white, incubated by female; hatch 28–29 days

- **YOUNG**
Nestling short white down; male brings food and after aprox. 2 weeks also helps to feed young; leave nest aprox. 30–35 days

- **FOOD**
Chiefly insects, plus small mammals, birds and worms

- **VOICE**
Shrill plaintive '*kioo*', barking '*werro*' etc.

- **HABITAT**
Open country, especially farmland, rocky places and wasteland

- **FLIGHT TIMES**
Most active at dawn and dusk, but may well be seen during the day

- **DISTRIBUTION**
England, Wales, extreme south of Scotland

- **STATUS**
Despite cyclical changes, probably fairly stable

LITTLE OWLS IN THE BRITISH ISLES

Underparts are pale grey-buff with prominent dark brown streaks.

Distribution Map Key

- Present all year round
- Present during summer months
- Present during winter months
- Not present

The little owl has strong curved toes on short legs.

During the day the little owl's flight is undulating – probably to avoid predators. By night however, its flight is direct and low over the ground.

The little owl is about the size of a song thrush – substantially smaller than the other British owls. It is only half the size of the tawny owl, which often takes it for food. Although the little owl lacks the conspicuous facial disc which characterises most owls, it has prominent pale 'eyebrows' and splendid golden-yellow eyes. Its plumage is mottled brown and white.

Of all British owls, the little owl is the most likely to be seen by daylight. It is often active during the day – although it still prefers to hunt at dusk or dawn. The owl's most frequently heard call is a loud ringing '*kioo-kioo*'. The young make a wheezing sound when calling for food.

The little owl's diet is quite different from that of the other, much larger, owls in this country. It principally feeds on insects such as beetles, craneflies and earwigs, as well as earthworms and small rodents. Other birds are seldom prey items except during the nesting season, when the owl may take blackbirds and house sparrows.

When hunting, the owl usually watches for prey from a low perch such as a fence post, dropping down with talons spread at any sign of movement. It will also run along the ground in pursuit of prey – it runs fast, though it cuts a rather comic figure doing so.

The little owl's diet was the subject of an early scientific survey by the British Trust for Ornithology, and this may well have contributed to its survival in Britain. As the owl spread rapidly from county to county it became the victim of increasing numbers of gamekeepers, who claimed that it was a major predator of pheasant and partridge chicks. Although the survey showed that the owl took the occasional game bird chick, these formed a very small part of its diet – which was based mainly on farmland pests.

The fluffy owlets later grow feathers and often appear at the entrance of the nest to be fed by their parents. This continues for several weeks, even after the young have fledged.

THE WISE OLD OWL

'The wise old owl sat in an oak, the more he heard the less he spoke. The less he spoke the more he heard, why can't we all be like that bird?'

What links this old rhyme with a leader in a youth movement? With a 13th century poem? With a character who was friendly with a bear and a donkey? And with the capital of Greece?

Not too difficult to guess – the main link is, of course, owls. But an extra mark should be awarded for saying that they refer to owls as symbols of wisdom and learning. 'Brown Owl' is the leader of a Brownie pack. *The Owl and the Nightingale* is a 13th century allegorical poem, and Owl is the much loved companion of Christopher Robin and his friends – who prides himself on his rather wobbly powers of spelling.

Today owls of all species are regarded as symbols of wisdom. Perhaps this is because of their their upright posture and their amazing eyes, which seem to look right through us. Or perhaps it's because they look a bit like us, as we're sure we are wise!

The owl's staring eyes make its penetrating gaze seem all-knowing. Like humans and monkeys (which also have forward-facing eyes) they seem more alert and understanding than many other creatures.

The owl was the symbol of Pallas Athene – the patron of Athens and goddess of wisdom. As we can see from ancient coins, her owl wasn't just any owl, but the little owl. The scientific name it bears today, *Athene noctua*, confirms that the little owl is the goddess's real 'wise old owl'.

Farmland is the little owl's favourite habitat, including cultivated fields with hedges, parks, and wasteland with scattered trees. It is seldom found in mountainous areas or dense woodland. By far the most common nest site is a hole in a deciduous tree, with occasional nests in buildings, cliffs or rabbit burrows. They also use nest boxes.

The male owl claims his territory early in the year and starts calling for a female in March. As she perches near the nest hole, he flies round and round her, and then copulates. Sometimes they both chase swiftly to and fro across their territory.

A FAITHFUL PAIR

Little owls clean out the nest hole but do not make a nest as such. Only the female incubates, though some males stay in the nest hole while she lays her eggs. Little owls seem to be faithful to their territory and to each other, as long as both the pair survive.

Almost all little owls' eggs are laid in April and May, peaking at the end of April – the shortest breeding season of any European owl. It seldom lays a second clutch, or even replaces one that has been lost. The eggs, usually between three and five in number, are white, matt and elliptical in shape. Incubation usually starts as soon as the first egg has been laid but, unusually for an owl, may sometimes be postponed until the clutch has been completed.

When the young hatch, it has been suggested that the male bird feeds them as well as the female. If true, this is also unusual among owls. Most feeding takes place from dusk to midnight then, after a gap of two hours, continues until dawn. Little hunting takes place during the day.

The young leave the nest after about 30–35 days, but may stay in the nest hole by day long after this. Owlets are able to fly a week after leaving the nest, though their parents may continue to feed them for up to a month. Many of the young owls die within their first few months, but if they survive beyond four months they probably become mature within one year. Individuals of this species have been known to live for up to 17 years.

Most little owls nest in tree hollows, although some do nest in cliff holes or in man-made structures. They will use a nest box, but not if it has gaps where the light can get in. Pairs can be very faithful to their nest site.

Feeding the family

At first the nestlings are fed only by their mother but later the father also helps. Weighing about 11 g at hatching, they grow very rapidly for the first ten days, then slightly more slowly – until by day 16 they weigh about two-thirds of the adult weight.

1 & 2 Perched on a post or other prominent place, the little owl watches intently for movement which might indicate suitable prey on the ground below. When something is spotted, it leaps downward, keeping its eye on the prey. Little owls hunt mainly at dusk and dawn.

The female owl feeds the oldest and largest chick first. She shelters it with her wing as she does so. If food is short this may be the only survivor.

A LIGHT SNACK

Owls do eat other owls – after all, they are a meal on the wing like any other bird. In Britain the little owl is the most likely victim, which is hardly surprising as it's our smallest owl. Although a barn owl is sometimes the killer, it's much more likely to be a tawny, which seems to have a definite preference for little owls.

On the continent the greatest owl killer is the huge, aggressive eagle owl, not normally found in Britain. This has been known to kill all the other 12 European owls – the long-eared being its principal victim – as well as 18 daytime birds of prey and even an adult owl of its own species.

Apart from the eagle and the tawny however, most other owls which are capable of killing smaller species (the great grey, snowy, hawk, and long- and short-eared owls) seldom do so. So why are some owls more tolerant than others? It seems that aggressive owls remain in the same territory year after year, and defend from all comers those areas where they rest and hunt their prey. Owls which migrate or wander freely are not under the same pressure. However, little owls are too small to count as rivals – they're just a light snack!

3 The wings spread backwards into a V shape and control the speed of descent as the legs and feet are stretched out to capture the prey. This might be an insect, small mammal or a small bird.

4 The feet are the owl's main weapons in hunting food and they are spread wide open as the bird descends. The talons are razor sharp and they grasp the prey as the bird lands on the ground. This, plus the weight of the bird, ensures that the prey is killed almost instantly.

5 The food is carried off in the beak to be eaten at leisure elsewhere or fed to young in the nest. Hard parts of the prey such as bones or insect wings do not pass through the body but are separated from the soft parts in the stomach and regurgitated as pellets. These may collect under a regular perch.

Nesting and roosting inside hollow trees give at least some protection to little owls.

Long-eared owl – the great pretender

Although this owl's characteristic feathery 'ears' might look impressive, they're actually not ears at all! In fact, its real ears lie hidden below the feathers of its face. This seldom-seen owl has a range of visual and behavioural 'tricks', which help it to outwit any potential intruders.

THE LONG-EARED OWL'S 'EARS' aren't really ears, but are simply ear-tufts and have nothing to do with hearing at all. Nevertheless, they do fulfil a definite function, helping other birds to recognise the owl and breaking up its distinctive owlish silhouette when it is hoping to spend the day roosting unobserved in a tree. Although the long-eared's ear tufts are so conspicuous however – even downy chicks in the nest already show signs of them – it sometimes holds them flat, particularly when it is in flight.

The openings to the actual ears are large, and they are situated asymmetrically under the edge of the facial disk, providing the owl with excellent directional hearing. The owl's other conspicuous feature, its magnificent orange eyes, makes it a popular subject in wildlife photography. Over most of its considerable range, its plumage is basically rich brown, but in Britain it tends to have a greyish cast. The complex pattern of streaking and mottling provides highly efficient camouflage among barks and lichens, enabling the long-eared to be the least observed and probably the least known of the British owls.

This handsome owl carries out a number

The owl's ear tufts may not be used for hearing, but they help to break up the tell-tale 'owl' silhouette. This helps the birds to remain undetected, even in winter when the leaves are gone from the trees.

of dramatic displays, sometimes as part of courtship, sometimes to defend its nest against potential enemies. Early in the breeding season the male performs a spectacular display flight to encourage a female to accept him. Often he begins with a period of quiet hooting from a song post. Then, taking off into the trees, he circles round and round the breeding area with slow wing beats, periodically clapping his wings together. Sometimes the female flies up to join him in a session of formation flying and synchronous wing clapping. This display frequently culminates in copulation.

Although the long-eared owl is not a particularly aggressive bird, it has some effective strategies for defending its nest. One such tactic is 'injury feigning'. This is when it flies directly into the intruder, just avoiding collision at the last moment and crashing to the ground below, before sud-

WHAT A HOOT!

The long-eared owl has a fine repertoire of songs and calls. It is notoriously difficult to describe birds' sounds, but Heimo Mikkola, the well-known authority on European owls, has collected various comparisons made by ornithologists. For example, the male's territorial hoot has been compared with blowing across the top of a bottle – and indeed this strategy can be used to attract the owl's attention. The female's quieter

The long-eared owl saves its wide variety of calls for the breeding season.

call is thought to sound like a lamb, or like blowing through a paper and comb. A brood of small young in the nest reminds one ornithologist of the jingling of small coins, while older young calling for food are generally agreed to sound like a squeaky gate. Outside the breeding season, the long-eared owl is usually silent.

The young owls' plumage may be nothing to write home about – though it provides perfect camouflage – but already their orange eyes are dazzling.

LONG-EARED OWL FACT FILE

Although the long-eared's eyes are brilliant orange-yellow, its grey-brown plumage is highly effective as camouflage against barks and lichens. Unlike its cousin, the short-eared owl, the long-eared is a shy, nocturnal bird. These two features combined make it one of Britain's most rarely-seen owls.

● **NAMES**
English name: Long-eared owl
Scientific name: *Asio otus*

● **SIZE**
36 cm;
200–400 g

● **KEY FEATURES**
Britain's only medium-sized owl with long ear-tufts – not seen in flight; orange-yellow eyes; plumage mottled buff/grey-brown

● **NEST**
Old nest of another bird, especially crow and magpie; occasionally nest on the ground and will also accept man-made nesting baskets

● **BREEDING**
March to early June;
single-brooded

● **EGGS**
3–5 eggs, white, elliptical; mainly incubated by female, 27–28 days

● **YOUNG**
Nestlings covered in dense white down; leave nest 23–24 days; fly 10 days later; independent at 12–13 weeks

● **FOOD**
Chiefly small rodents, also birds and insects

● **VOICE**
Long, moaning hoot, also barking call; older owlets have hunger call like hinges of a squeaky gate

● **HABITAT**
Coniferous woodland, small plantations, shelter belts, etc; also hunts in adjacent open country, heaths, marshes and sand dunes

● **FLIGHT TIMES**
Nocturnal

● **DISTRIBUTION**
Widely distributed, but scarce in much of England and Wales, especially South West; commonest owl in Ireland; winter visitors from Europe

● **STATUS**
Widespread but patchy; population may be affected by competition with tawny owls and fluctuations in number of voles, its main food

Distribution Map Key

- Present all year round
- Present during summer months
- Present during winter months
- Not present

LONG-EARED OWLS IN THE BRITISH ISLES

The owl's 'ears' are simply tufts of feathers, and have nothing to do with hearing. The openings of the real ears are positioned behind the facial disc.

The brown-grey, streaked plumage provides excellent camouflage against bark and lichens.

---

denly 'recovering' and flying off. Another strategy is used by owls in or near the nest – even by owlets when their parents are absent. This time the owl tries to frighten the intruder away by making itself look as huge and ferocious as possible. It puffs out all its feathers to double its size, spreads out its wings like a large umbrella behind its head, and fixes the intruder with fierce orange eyes – enough to deter all but the most determined of predators!

DINNER ON THE DOORSTEP
Long-eared owls are widespread throughout Britain, although they are unevenly distributed. One reason for this may be the shortage of their preferred conifer habitat, although major afforestation in recent years should be to their benefit. Another factor may be competition with the larger and highly successful tawny, Britain's commonest owl. In Ireland, where there are no tawnies, the long-eared prospers.

In some ways the long-eared owl resembles the tawny: both are active by night and both live in woodlands. However, the long-eared's preferred habitat differs in certain ways. It typically lives in 'islands' of woodland

After hatching, the young climb or jump out of the nest, though they are not yet able to fly. Their parents feed them until they are two months old.

(usually conifers) in open country: copses, thickets, shelter belts, isolated clumps of trees, or perhaps on the edge of larger woods. As the long-eared owl finds most of its prey animals (small rodents) out in the fields, it prefers to have them on its doorstep, so to speak. In winter, when voles and mice are less available, British long-eareds are able to obtain a higher proportion of their diet from birds instead.

NESTING

The long-eared owl doesn't build a nest of its own, but will take over the old nest of another bird. These can range in size from a jay's nest to a heron's, but the owl most commonly uses the nest of a carrion crow or magpie. Sometimes the owl uses a squirrel's drey and it may also nest on the ground. Long-eared owls will also accept simulated twig nests based on willow baskets or hanging baskets designed for flowers, and these can be valuable in areas where natural nests are scarce.

The usual clutch is three to five eggs, incubated for around four weeks. If she is disturbed however, the female may abandon them, laying a replacement clutch later.

Short-eared owl – the wanderer

The short-eared owl is the scarcest of our five principal owls, though possibly the easiest to see as it is active during the day, hunting over open country. Look out for it in early winter, when the short-eared visitors arrive from Scandinavia!

SHORT- AND LONG-EARED OWLS ARE real long-distance travellers. In autumn and early winter, Scandinavian owls of these species find their homeland deep in snow and their prey inaccessible, so they head south and west to milder areas. Owls in the southernmost part of their range (including those in Britain) are able to stay put for the winter, but many migrating owls travel a 1,000 kilometres or more, across the North Sea to the east coast of Britain. There may be only a few hundred migrants, as numbers depend on the availability of voles, the owls' principal food. But occasionally thousands of these two species will arrive, and mixed parties can be seen recovering from their journeys in the shelter of coastal scrub and woodlands. The arrival of these winter migrants can boost the total short-eared population in Britain and Ireland from between 2,000–30,000 individuals.

COUNTRY COUSINS

As the short- and long-eared owls are closely related, it is not surprising that they have many similarities – although there are many contrasts too. One of the most striking is their habitat. While the long-eared typically lives in clumps of woodland, the short-eared prefers open country. As it is active during the day it may well be seen patrolling open grassland or hovering like a kestrel, raising its wings sharply to drop down on prey.

And while the long-eared is well known for its wide range of calls, the short-eared is not

Ground-nesting owlets are particularly at risk from predators. They shelter in the long grass and wait for their mother to bring food.

The short-eared owl can be seen only a couple of metres about the ground, ranging up and down open grassland and young forestry plantations in search of small mammals.

SHORT-EARED OWL FACT FILE

The short-eared owl has much smaller ear-tufts than its long-eared cousin, and they are only likely to be visible when the owl is agitated or curious. It is rather larger than the long-eared, and in flight the dark brown marks on the 'elbows' of its long wings are conspicuous.

● **NAMES**
English name: Short-eared owl
Scientific name: *Asio flammeus*

● **SIZE**
38 cm; 260–425 g

● **KEY FEATURES**
Ear-tufts hardly visible; dark feathers surround striking yellow eyes; plumage buffish-brown with streaked underparts; perches in slanting position rather than upright

● **NEST**
Scrape on ground sheltered by heather, reeds or bushes

● **BREEDING**
April–June/July; may have 2 broods when voles are abundant

● **EGGS**
4–8 eggs, white, almost spherical; incubated by female, 24–29 days

● **YOUNG**
Nestling covered by creamy buff down; young scatter in vegetation after 12–17 days; fly 2 weeks later; independent at 9–11 weeks

● **FOOD**
Principally small mammals, plus small birds and insects

● **VOICE**
Deep repeated hoot and high 'sneezing' bark

● **HABITAT**
Open country-moorland, bogs, marshes and dunes

● **FLIGHT TIMES**
Most likely medium-sized owl to be seen by day

● **DISTRIBUTION**
Resident and winter visitor; chiefly northern England and Scotland, scattered population West Wales and coastal areas of East Anglia, not yet established in Ireland

● **STATUS**
Prone to marked fluctuations linked to cycles of prey abundance, but no long-term changes apparent

SHORT-EARED OWLS IN THE BRITISH ISLES

Whereas the long-eared has striking orange eyes, the short-eared's are bright yellow, surrounded by dark feathers.

Plumage is buff-coloured, tinged with brown.

To spot the short-eared in flight, look out for dark brown markings on its 'elbows' and paler patches towards the ends of its wings

Distribution Map Key

- Present all year round
- Present during summer months
- Present during winter months
- Not present

---

a great songster. The owlets, too, are far less vocal than most young owls that live in woodlands. The male's territorial song consists of a series of '*hoo-hoo-hoos*', to which the female responds with a low harsh call.

While the long-eared owl generally uses the old nest of another large bird, the short-eared owl nests on the ground. Its chief requirement seems to be open country with a suitable food supply, and the nest is usually a shallow hollow sheltered by tall grass, reeds, heather and bushes.

The young owls in their ground nest are very vulnerable to predators such as carrion crows and foxes. Fortunately, they develop quickly, increasing their weight by 300 per

cent in the first five days after hatching, and by the same amount over the following five days. If food is scarce the largest owlet will eat the smallest – in this way at least some of the brood survive. The young usually leave the nest before they are fully fledged, sheltering in nearby vegetation. Their mother brings them food until they are able to fly at about

four weeks old. During the winter, the owls often gather in communal roosts, usually on the ground in the shelter of heather and undergrowth, although sometimes in woodland as long-eareds do.

Owls swallow their prey whole and later regurgitate pellets of undigested bones and fur. These become weathered in the open so that the bones stick out prominently.

IN SEARCH OF VOLES

In Britain, short-tailed voles make up to 83 per cent of the short-eared owl's diet. Where these are not available it turns to pygmy shrews, wood mice and brown rats.

But the fact remains that voles are still the staple diet – so what happens when there just aren't enough? Short-eareds maintain their diet of voles by migrating to places where their favourite food is abundant. Sometimes this is seasonal in response to severe winter weather. They are real

nomads however, and will also wander widely at other times of year when they are not nesting.

The breeding success of many owls is affected by peaks and troughs in the population of their prey, and this is certainly true of the short-eared. In a 'good vole year' they produce large clutches of eggs and will occasionally raise second broods, but when voles are scarce they lay much smaller clutches and may not breed at all.

Short-eared owls are great travellers; many will travel up to 1,000 km from Scandinavia to Britain to spend the winter.

Snowy owl – visitor from the Arctic

The huge white owl of the Arctic is adapted to open, treeless tundra, feeds on voles and small rodents, and endures long, dark winters of extreme cold. Nevertheless, it does turn up occasionally in Britain and has even bred here in the Shetlands.

THE SNOWY OWL IS A BIRD OF the far north. Its home is the Arctic tundra, amidst vast expanses of bleak, treeless landscape, patched with snow – especially those regions bordering the Arctic Ocean. In winter, most snowies head south to avoid the bitter cold and deep snow of their breeding grounds. Periodically however, the populations of small rodents that form the major part of the owls' diet drop dramatically, forcing the owls to move much further south than usual in search of some other food supply. These journeys take them down to central Europe, central Asia and the northern United States. The occasional snowy owl that arrives in Shetland has very likely made a considerable journey to get there – snowies are great wanderers.

Snowies are the largest and rarest of our British owls and many people would say that they are the most magnificent. Their average wingspan is nearly 150 cm and their weight just under 2 kg. Like most owls, the female snowy is larger and heavier

Like many predatory birds, the snowy owl begins to incubate as soon as the first egg is laid. This means that one chick often hatches several days earlier than the next. This will always be the biggest chick in the family.

At first young snowy owls are dark grey and speckled. They then acquire their white faces and some white feathers in their wings, but remain well camouflaged while they are in the nest.

◄In their treeless habitat, snowy owls use boulders and hummocks from which to survey their surroundings. These are also used as as roosting places.

SNOWY OWL FACT FILE

One of the largest of all owls, often active in full daylight, flying low like a huge white ghost. The snowy is also unusual as the two sexes have clearly different plumage. The male is almost totally white and the female is white with substantial dark markings.

● **NAMES**
English name: Snowy owl
Scientific name: *Nyctea scandiaca*

● **SIZE**
Male: 59 cm; 1,725 g
Female: 62 cm; 2,250 g

● **KEY FEATURES**
Huge, largely white; yellow eyes; female noticeably larger than male with black and brown barring; buzzard-like flight; often seen on ground

● **NEST**
Shallow scrape in ground, usually on slightly raised site to give views of surrounding area

● **BREEDING**
Variable, dependent on altitude, weather, etc; may be as early as mid-April, more usually mid-May in south of range; June in north

● **EGGS**
Eggs white, rounded; average clutch 3–9, but up to 14 when food supply is good; incubation by female, usually 30–33 days

● **YOUNG**
Young covered with short, thick white down, leave nest 14–28 days, fly 4 weeks later; independent at 15–17 weeks

● **FOOD**
Small and medium-sized rodents up to size of Arctic hare, including voles and lemmings; birds up to size of eider; on Shetland, rabbits and birds

● **VOICE**
Harsh bark, deep hoot; silent outside breeding season

● **HABITAT**
Tundra, high northern moorlands

● **FLIGHT TIMES**
Prefers night, but will hunt by day when nights are short

● **DISTRIBUTION**
Circumpolar, in tundra zone; periodically moves south to central Europe, central Asia and northern United States

● **STATUS**
Considered endangered, but population trends hard to assess

Golden staring eyes are emphasised by a dark rim.

The bill is black, unusual among owls, and partly hidden by feathers.

Feet covered in thick feathers to protect them from the cold and also from bites of prey.

PROTECTED!

The snowy owl is afforded special protection under Schedule One of the Wildlife and Countryside Act, 1981. It is an offence to disturb them at the nest without a licence.

---

than the male, but unusually, the male and female snowies can also be distinguished by the differences in their plumage. The adult male is virtually pure white, while the female is largely white but abundantly barred with brown or grey markings. Both have striking lemon-yellow eyes.

Snowy owls are usually seen perched on the ground, either horizontally or sitting upright, looking like large cats. In fact, in many languages they are described as 'cat owls'. In the Shetlands the name for the snowy is 'catogle'.

SURVIVING IN THE SNOW

Considering the severe climate in which snowy owls spend their lives, it is not surprising that they are excellently adapted to survive the cold. Their plumage is particularly thick and downy, and their legs and black beaks are virtually covered in feathers to conserve body heat. When food supplies permit, snowy owls will continue to breed in the same area from year to year, but how do they manage to raise a family in such a bleak, exposed situation?

Snowies usually site their nests on slight hummocks or rocky outcrops, giving the incubating females a good view over the surrounding countryside and approaching predators such as swooping skuas. Both the

Snowy owls nest on open ground, relying on their own size and ferocity for defence against predators. The grey, fluffy chicks resemble rocks or lumps of earth, making them less conspicuous.

▼ *The male hunts for food which he brings back to the nest for the female and chicks. In the Arctic he catches mainly voles, but in Shetland the menu includes mostly birds, and also voles and rabbits.*

male and female help to make the nest – scraping out a slight hollow which they often line with bits of moss and grass. The nest will usually be in the lee of a rock but is sometimes out in the open. In these conditions one might expect a sitting owl to be dangerously conspicuous, but this is not the case. As the female does most of the incubation, the dark barring on her white plumage breaks up her outline, providing excellent camouflage in the landscape of snowy tundra and scattered rocks.

The male snowy claims his territory with a loud harsh call; the female's call is similar but at a higher pitch. He presents her with

Snowy owls have been known to visit Scotland occasionally since the early 19th century. In 1963 there was a sudden increase in their numbers, and over

Although protected, snowy owls have not become established in Britain. They have nested and reared young in Shetland, but no male snowies have visited for several years.

the next few years snowies were reported from Shetland, Orkney and a few even further south.

The great excitement came in 1967 however, when snowy owls bred for the first time on the island of Fetlar in Shetland – the first ever proved breeding in Britain. Five young were successfully reared, and the same pair (presumably) continued to breed up until 1975. From

1973 to 1975 two females attempted to breed, but the single male was unable to provide enough food for both and one nest was deserted each year. During this period 20 young owls were reared – six males and 14 females. By spring 1976 the male had disappeared, and though there have been up to four female owls on Fetlar each year, no new male has turned up to join them since then.

pieces of food from her beak, then whole mice, and finally at about five weeks old they are able to deal with larger prey for themselves. As tiny chicks the owls make a high-pitched whistle which they continue to use – gradually becoming louder and stronger – even after they have learned to fly. Their parents can hear it far away from the nest.

food and invites her to mate by adopting the 'angel' position – lowering his head and half raising his wings. Copulation usually follows.

Incubating and rearing the young is a long and tedious job for snowies, especially the female. An average clutch has between four and nine eggs, but in years when food is abundant she may lay 11 eggs or even more. As laying and incubation are staggered, the female may be on duty at the nest for seven to eight weeks. Even after all the eggs are hatched, she must continue to brood the chicks under her warm plumage until they are able to regulate their own temperature.

While the young are in the nest the male snowy hunts to feed the whole family, but the owlets are fed exclusively by their mother. At first she offers them small

DEFENDING THE YOUNG

When danger threatens, the snowy's first reaction is to try to fade into the landscape. It closes its conspicuous eyes to a slit, then stands upright and fluffs out its feathers. If the nest is threatened, both parents play a part in defending it. When the young are small the male is the main aggressor, hooting and swooping on the intruder to drive it away. The female performs a distraction display, flailing about on the ground and screeching as if injured. Once the young have left the nest however, she will also become aggressive in defence of the owlets, diving down on enemies and striking them with her wings.

Living as they do in areas devoid of trees, snowy owls generally use low vantage points such as rocks and hummocks to watch out for prey. When a snowy sees movement it

Sometimes six or more chicks may hatch from particularly large clutches, but snowies usually lay four to six eggs, depending on food availability.

This female is carrying off her latest victim – a king eider duck.

A male snowy owl is a handsome bird, pure white except for a few faint greyish-brown marks on its back. These often fade to cream in late summer.

WILDLIFE WATCH

DID YOU KNOW?

● It seems that a pair of snowy owls seldom remains faithful for life. Males are known to have two females at the same time, including the one that nested in Shetland. Females may also have more than one partner.

● From ten days old, the chick has a distinctive pale mark on the darker down of its face, rather like an X. At 18-days-old its face is darker and the X has become larger and more distinct.

● Snowy owls breed well in captivity and they can be seen in most zoos and bird collections. Although primarily an Arctic species, it seems that this bird is very flexible and can cope with the British climate.

either drops down on the animal or else pursues it on foot, holding onto the prey until it is pecked or crushed to death. Surplus food is generally stored in caches around the nest site.

The snowy owl shows a strong disposition to be a 'night owl', preferring to be active and particularly to hunt during the hours of darkness. But as it mostly lives in the Arctic where there is virtually no darkness in summer, it must often be active in daylight. Whatever the season however, the snowy owl continues to roost during 'real' night time. It has been suggested that the owl's periods of activity are governed by the activity patterns of the animals that form their principal sources of food.

JET SET OWLS

The relationship between mankind and the snowy owl goes back thousands of years. A carving of a pair of snowy owls and their young was found in the most remote part of the Trois Frères cave in France – a place devoted to religious rituals. And the numbers of owl bones at Neolithic dwelling sites show that snowies were a regular part of the diet.

Today, snowy owls and human beings still live side by side – but now they meet in the air! Every few years food supplies fail in the snowies' Arctic breeding grounds and they head south in search of a place where small rodents are plentiful. Toronto International Airport just fits the bill – expanses of open grassland, voles in abundance and gantries, poles and cable drums for the owls to perch on. This is fine for the owls, but it causes great problems for the airport. In one year over 850 bird strikes were recorded in Canada, causing $300 million worth of damage and considerable danger to passengers and crew.

The answer came in the form of a falconer with a golden eagle. When an aircraft is about to take off, the falconer is called and he releases the eagle to patrol over the runway. No injury is done to the snowy owls or to the other birds in the area: they simply scatter at the sight of the 'king of the birds', leaving the runway clear for takeoff.

And what are those animals? Contrary to what used to be believed, lemmings are not the commonest item in many snowies' diets. Studies in Scandinavia have shown that two thirds of snowies' prey consists of various types of vole and only one third of lemmings. On Shetland, where there are no lemmings, three quarters of prey animals were rabbits, the rest being various sorts of birds. It seems that in their frequent wanderings, snowies adapt to feed on whatever animals are readily available.

The female guards the chicks and feeds them on birds and small mammals brought back to her by the male. Small mammals are eaten whole, but larger prey will be torn to pieces to give to the chicks.

The snowy owl has less broad wings than other species and its flight is very reminiscent of a buzzard (which is a similar size). The barn owl is the only other mainly white owl, but it is a much smaller bird.

Owls of continental Europe

The six owls we see in Britain are also found elsewhere in Europe, but others are found there that we are unlikely to see here in the wild. These include one that kills all other species of owl, one that catches voles under the snow, and one that disguises itself as a tree trunk!

Many European owls live deep in remote forests. The great grey will continue to incubate her eggs in deepest winter, when she may be almost buried in snow.

Eagle owl – the mighty hunter

One of the largest aerial predators, the eagle owl is big enough to kill a roe deer fawn. They are found in woodlands over most of Europe, but not in Britain.

The eagle owl is a typical looking owl with large eyes and heavily feathered legs.

The owl's impressive wings are almost two metres across.

EAGLE OWLS ARE THE LARGEST and most powerful owls in Europe. They are found through much of the world, but in Europe there are 10 races, varying in size and colouring. The massive owl of the Urals is the largest, weighing up to four kilograms, with a wingspan of nearly two metres and large orange eyes. Heading south from northern Scandinavia through to the Mediterranean they become smaller and darker. As usual in owls, the female is substantially larger than the male, but in this species the two sexes can also be distinguished by their ear-tufts. In the male these are fairly upright, while the female's are horizontal or slightly drooping.

Eagle owls have a monotonous 'oohoo' call, higher pitched in the female. A pair will call excitedly to each other from one part of their territory to another, and on a still night they can be heard three or four kilometres away. Couples pair for life and the female lays her eggs early in the spring, often while snow is still on the ground. The owlets continue to be partly dependent on their parents for several months after they leave the nest, learning to hunt over the milder months while prey is plentiful. Later chicks often die unless food is abundant.

A FEARSOME KILLER

The eagle owl is the most aggressive owl in Europe. It has a wide choice of prey, including insects, birds of varying sizes, and even mammals as large as a roe deer fawn. Some specialise in particular prey, such as hedgehogs, stripping off the skin and spikes before eating the flesh. Eagle owls are also known to kill all species of European owl and 18 daytime birds of prey. They even kill other eagle owls.

Traditionally an owl of wilderness areas, especially mountain tops and vast coniferous forests, the eagle owl is now adapting to live close to rubbish dumps. Today it finds much of its food in cultivated areas.

EAGLE OWL FACT FILE

● NAMES
English name: Eagle owl
Scientific name: *Bubo bubo*

● SIZE
65 cm–70 cm; male from 1,500 g, female up to 4 kg

● KEY FEATURES
Huge, prominent eartufts; broadly-streaked, tawny breast; upper parts mottled; large, orange eyes

● NEST
Hollow among rocks and scrub, in hollow trees, old nests of birds of prey

● BREEDING
Begins mid-March in south, early May in north

● EGGS
2, 3 or 4 eggs; incubation by female 34–36 days

● YOUNG
Leave nest 40 days; independent 20–25 weeks; single brooded

● FOOD
Wide range of prey, from small birds to larger

mammals; takes all species of owl and many diurnal birds of prey

● VOICE
Deep 'oohoo' and 'keck, keck' calls

● HABITAT
Dense forests, rocky gorges on mountains, even deserts; now starting to live closer to human habitation

● FLIGHT TIMES
Strictly nocturnal

● DISTRIBUTION
Eagle owls are widespread over most of the world; 10 races in Europe, extending from north Scandinavia to Mediterranean; not native in Britain

● STATUS
Until recently one of Europe's most endangered owls; now under special protection and breeding population is on the increase

Prominent eartufts, orange eyes and massive size are distinguishing features.

HERE TOO?

Eagle owls already breed over much of continental Europe, so why not here too? There are several records of individuals in Britain, some going back to the 19th century. Reports have become more frequent in recent years, but most of these birds probably escaped or were released. Eagle owls are often kept in captivity, but are expensive to maintain and may be set free to fend for themselves.

In 1987, a pair of feral eagle owls reared a chick in this country. There have been several more breeding attempts, in Scotland and the Peak District. The prospect of these splendid birds nesting in Britain is exciting, but it could be a mixed blessing. Eagle owls are such powerful killers that they would have a devastating effect on wildlife. Some kill all other owls that enter their territory, which could be a serious hazard for native British owls.

Great grey owl – the snow diver

Thick layers of feathers make this northern owl seem far larger than it actually is, but it needs this abundant insulation to survive the bitter cold of its forest home.

Great grey chicks take up to five months to become fully independent.

WHEN YOU COMPARE THE great grey with the eagle owl, Europe's largest owl, you get a bit of a surprise. The great grey looks much the same size, perhaps slightly larger, but if you could persuade both these huge birds to sit on scales you would soon discover the difference. The great grey actually weighs only half as much as the eagle owl, as much of its bulk is made up of thick layers of feathers. Living in the damp, mossy forests of northern Europe, which are deep in snow for much of the year, the great grey needs this abundant insulation to maintain body heat, and for the females to incubate their eggs and protect their young from the extreme cold.

The great grey has a huge head (the size of a child's), small yellow eyes and the largest, most symmetrical facial disc of any owl. Although it can see well, even in bright sunshine, it usually hunts by its highly sensitive hearing. The ear openings are sited asymmetrically under the edges of the facial disc, enabling the owl to pinpoint the exact position of its prey (usually voles) as they

DEVOTED MOTHER

Females lay up to six eggs – often in the untidy twig nests of large birds of prey.

Few incubating birds can have a more bleak and uncomfortable task than the great grey owl. The female sits on her eggs for 24 hours a day, in snow and rain, with night temperatures dropping to -20 C, only occasionally turning the eggs and resettling herself. An intensive study of one particular female found that for two weeks after the oldest chick hatched, she remained on the nest for 99 per cent of the time, only leaving her post briefly to eject a pellet.

The female's well-feathered body enables her to build up warmth for incubation, and to protect her chicks from the bitter cold of the outside world. As well as keeping the chicks warm and dry, she also preens them and eats their pellets to keep the nest clean. She has no need to go hunting, as the male brings food both for her and for her to feed the chicks.

An incubating female is alert, but not aggressive. She looks down at intruders and claps her bill to drive them away. Once she has chicks however, she becomes ferocious – fearlessly attacking intruders and slashing with her powerful talons. Several people who have approached to examine a great grey nest have suffered the loss of an eye or other serious injuries.

GREAT GREY OWL FACT FILE

- **NAMES**
English name: Great grey owl
Scientific name: *Strix nebulosa*

- **SIZE**
68 cm; males average 900 g, females 1200 g

- **KEY FEATURES**
Huge – almost as long as eagle owl but less bulky; large round head, conspicuous facial disc, small yellow eyes; plumage grey with darker streaks

- **NEST**
Old twig nests of large birds of prey, stump of tree, ground or cliff

- **BREEDING**
Begins mid-April; may not nest in unfavourable years

- **EGGS**
3–6 eggs; incubation by female 28–30 days

- **YOUNG**
Leave nest 20–28 days; independent 18–22 weeks

- **FOOD**
Largely voles, often seized by

Concentric dark rings around small yellow eyes are a distinctive feature.

owl plunging into snow to reach them below surface

- **VOICE**
Deep, booming '*hoo hoo hoo*'

- **HABITAT**
Dense conifer forests, though they hunt in open country

- **FLIGHT TIMES**
Often active during the day

- **DISTRIBUTION**
Breed round North Pole in Europe, Asia and North America; more southerly when populations low, (no records from Britain)

- **STATUS**
Once considered the rarest European owl, but recent records suggest it may be more abundant than previously thought

scamper unseen under the surface of the snow. The owl will hover briefly above the crucial spot, then drop with legs and talons extended. Sometimes it will plunge into the snow head first, and photographs have shown the impression of the owl's face and even its bill on the surface. Often the prey escapes, but if the pounce is successful, the vole is killed under the snow and the owl swallows it whole in a couple of seconds.

GENTLE GIANTS
Despite their huge size, great greys are not usually aggressive birds, except when the female is defending her young. They show little fear of man, and tolerate birds of prey and other owls on their territory – including their own species. This tolerant behaviour is typical of owls which seek a different territory each year.

Great greys usually nest in the old twig nests of big birds of prey, such as goshawks. Others prefer tree-stumps, and some nest on flat ground or even cliffs. No nest material is added. In their typical habitat of dense pine and spruce forest, they are not easy to locate, but they have also begun to nest near farmhouses and the edges of towns.

Ural owl – the tawny owl's cousin

Ural owls inhabit the great forests of Scandinavia and Russia. They resemble giant tawny owls, but will normally kill or drive away their smaller cousins.

In the breeding season Ural owls call loudly, from a perch or in flight.

THE URAL OWL BELONGS TO the same genus as the tawny and the great grey too. You can certainly see the 'family resemblance'! It looks like a large pale tawny, with a big, almost circular facial disc, small eyes and a long tail. The male has a variety of deep hooting calls, while the female at the nest makes an assortment of clucking, barking and hissing sounds.

Ural owls also resemble their tawny cousins in being sedentary – they don't wander widely like owls such as the short-eared. They maintain the same territories year after year, much larger than a tawny's, and choose a different nest site within their territory each season. They stay on their territories even during a poor vole year, when they may not breed.

The Ural owl owes its Swedish name, 'slaguggla', to the way the female defends the nest. It means 'attacking owl'. Like the tawny, the Ural drives owls and birds of prey off its territory. If Ural and tawny territories overlap, the Ural will usually kill or drive away the much smaller tawny, though they can sometimes live as peaceful neighbours.

OWL IN A BOX

Traditionally, Ural owls nest in the stumps and holes of old pine and spruce trees. In natural forests these trees break off a few metres above the ground, providing plenty of suitable nest sites. But in commercially run, modern forests, old and diseased trees are cleared, depriving the owls of their favourite nesting places.

Consequently, from the late 1950s Urals turned increasingly to their next choice – old twig nests built by other large birds, principally goshawks. In 1960, however, when concerned people in Finland started putting up nest boxes for homeless Ural owls, their offer was accepted with enthusiasm.

Within a few years, more nest boxes were being used than any other sort of nest site.

The situation remains the same today. Nest boxes are particularly popular in areas such as southern Finland, where populations are high, but less so in the north where there are still sufficient natural sites for the smaller number of owls. Nevertheless, as the number of Ural owls increases and they nest more and more in the proximity of human beings, man-made nest boxes remain important in all areas.

Ural owls rarely fly far and remain in the same woodland territory throughout the year.

URAL OWL FACT FILE

Unusually small eyes in a flat face create a rather gentle appearance for an owl.

● NAMES
English name: Ural owl
Scientific name: *Strix uralensis*

● SIZE
60 cm; male 650–800 g, female 600–1,000 g

● KEY FEATURES
Similar to tawny, but larger, paler and with longer tail; small dark eyes; facial disc greyish-white, unlined; underparts streaked with dark marks; tail barred

● NEST
In tree stumps, holes, old nests of birds of prey, nestboxes

● BREEDING
Starts mid to late March

● EGGS
2–4 eggs; incubation period 4–5 weeks

● YOUNG
Leave nest after about 25 days, independent 14–16 weeks

● FOOD
Small mammals; various birds

up to the size of black grouse, including other owls (especially Tengmalm's)

● VOICE
Deep hooting, frequently repeated

● HABITAT
Forests: coniferous, deciduous and mixed; sometimes in villages and near human habitation

● FLIGHT TIMES
Hunts by night, but also active by day

● DISTRIBUTION
Forest areas of north east Europe and north Asia

● STATUS
Population increasing in northern Europe, less prosperous in south

In the breeding season, Ural owls feed chiefly on voles when they are available, but birds make up 15 per cent of their diet. They take an extraordinary range, from goldcrest to black grouse – some 35 species in all. Other owls in their diet include long-eareds, Tengmalm's and Ural owl chicks, and they also eat frogs and insects. It is this ability to take advantage of so many available food sources that enables them to stay on their territories throughout the year.

FOREST OWLS

Urals are forest owls. They breed in mixed and conifer forests, hunting their prey on forest edges and in clearings (usually by night, but sometimes by day). They start to nest early in the year, and often have to clear the nest of snow. The female lays a clutch of two to four rounded, white eggs which she will incubate for four to five weeks. It is thought that they mate for life.

Ural owls are uncommon in central Europe, but to the north (in Finland, Norway, Sweden and Russia) their numbers are on the increase. They have not been recorded in Britain so far, and we are unlikely to see them here.

Hawk owl – the un-owlish owl

Despite its long tail, pointed wings and fearless disposition, the northern hawk owl is not a hawk, nor are the various unrelated hawk owls that live in the southern hemisphere. It's all in the name.

The hawk owl is active by day and will even hunt in bright sunlight.

THE HAWK OWL MIGHT HAVE been designed to confuse bird-watchers. Although it is certainly an owl, it lacks many typical features and has others – particularly the prominent black border to its facial disc – which make it appear distinctly hawk-like. It has a small head, rather flatter than most owls, smallish yellow eyes, a long tapering tail and short wings. Young hawk owls have a dark facial mask for the first few weeks after leaving the nest, which makes them look quite different from their parents. The male's principal call is a prolonged 'hoo-ooo-ooo', lasting up to 14 seconds, but between them the pair have a wide and varied repertoire.

The hawk owl is active by day and will

The hawk owl can often be seen in daylight and is fearless of observors. This female is brooding in a typical nest site on top of a broken tree stump.

even hunt in bright sunlight, either from a perch or hovering like a kestrel. Unlike most other owls it is primarily a daytime hunter, and relies not so much on its acute hearing as its sharp eyesight as it watches for rodents in the melting snow. It's not difficult to get a good view of this handsome owl, as it often perches conspicuously on a tree or telegraph pole. Like some other birds of the far north, the hawk owl is also unfamiliar with man and consequently fearless of human observers.

Hawk owls start nesting early in the year. Generally they tolerate birds of prey and other owls in their territory, although they are known to kill the smaller Tengmalm's owl. They are aggressive at the nest however. Both the adults will attack intruders, and the male is particularly dangerous when his mate is incubating or brooding the young.

FINDING FOOD

At this stage food requirements at the nest are not particularly great, but later on there may be a brood of eight or nine thriving young. These require plenty of food and there are estimates of 30 or more feeds in 24 hours. Many of these feeds occur during the day, as the hawk owl nests in the Arctic where there is not much real night

During the breeding season, voles will form more than 90 per cent of the hawk owl's diet, although surprisingly lemmings are not of great importance. It is clearly a real expert at finding voles when they are present in good numbers. Outside the owl's breeding season nearly one third of its diet consists of various birds, up to the size of a willow grouse.

HAWK OWL FACT FILE

● **NAMES**
English name: Hawk owl
Scientific name: *Surnia ulula*

● **SIZE**
35–40 cm; male 300 g, female heavier

● **KEY FEATURES**
Medium-sized, strange-looking owl, resembling hawk; prominent, dark border to facial disc, long tail and pointed wings, yellow eyes; crown and upper parts dark, barred white

● **NEST**
Broken-off stump or hole in tree, old nest of large bird

● **BREEDING**
Usually begins in April

● **EGGS**
4–9 eggs; incubation period 25–30 days

● **YOUNG**
Leave nest at 30–34 days, independent

approx. 15 weeks

● **FOOD**
Small mammals, especially voles, and various birds

● **VOICE**
Long, bubbling 'hoo-ooo-ooo', plus various other sounds

● **HABITAT**
Coniferous forest and open birch scrub

● **FLIGHT TIMES**
Hunts chiefly by day, perches conspicuously on top of tree or telegraph pole

● **DISTRIBUTION**
All round North Pole in Europe, America and Asia; very occasional visitor to Britain

● **STATUS**
Population in Europe fluctuates

Perched on top of a post or a broken tree stump, the hawk owl can look a bit like a fairy on a Christmas tree.

RARE VISITOR

Hawk owls are birds of the Arctic forests, spreading round the North Pole through Europe, Asia and North America. After a normal breeding season many of them will wander locally.

Every few years, however, a severe scarcity of their principal food, voles, will force them to head south and west – well beyond their usual range. Sometimes the owls will then settle down and breed far from home. It is in such years that the odd hawk owl may arrive in Britain, but it is a rare event and they have never been found breeding here.

Tengmalm's owl – forest hunter

Widespread in the dense, dark conifer forests of northern Europe, this tiny nocturnal predator feeds mainly on voles and other small mammals.

Chicks leave the nest and become fully independent of their mother when they are about 5–6 weeks old.

TENGMALM'S OWL IS SIMILAR IN size to the little owl but it has a much larger, rounded head, pronounced dark margins to the edge of its facial disc and yellow eyes. Tengmalm's owl is chiefly active at night and is dazzled by full sunlight. It's a specialist at hunting in dense, dark woodland, where its small size and nimble flight enable it to move skillfully through the trees, hardly brushing the vegetation. Although its vision is not as good as the sharp-eyed tawny owl's, it is far better than a human's – about 10 times better it's estimated.

Like many others owls, Tengmalm's nest in tree holes. Often these are the holes made by Europe's biggest woodpecker – the black woodpecker – which has never been recorded in the wild in Britain. As in the case of the Ural owl, all good bird watchers have come to the aid of the Tengmalm's owl. Noticing that the owls

CHOCOLATE COLOURED CHICKS

Young Tengmalm's owls bear little resemblance to their parents. At hatching they are covered with pale grey down, and their mother spends the day with them in the nest. When they reach three weeks old however, she starts to leave them for periods of time and joins the male – hunting and bringing back food.

Now the contrast can clearly be seen. While the adults have rufous brown upper parts and whitish facial discs and breasts, the young are dark chocolate brown all over, apart from pale marks around their eyes and bills. When the adults return to feed their young, they don't enter the nest but reach through the entrance hole, obscuring the light. But no problem – the pale marks on the chicks' faces help them to pop food into the appropriate beaks!

Young owlets are a distinctive brown colour, with white markings around their eyes and bills. As with many owls, one is older and larger than the others.

TENGMALMS OWL FACT FILE

Tengmalm's owl has a particularly large head that is squarish in shape.

● NAMES
English name: Tengmalm's owl
Scientific name: *Aegolius funereus*

● SIZE
25 cm; 90–170 g

● KEY FEATURES
Like little owl but much larger head; dark margins to facial disc, yellow eyes; direct flight; nocturnal; chocolate-brown juvenile unmistakable

● NEST
Woodpecker or natural holes in trees; nestboxes

● BREEDING
May start as early as end of February, but most eggs laid in April

● EGGS
3–7 eggs, incubation by female 25–32 days

● YOUNG
Leave nest 28–36 days; independent 10 weeks

● FOOD
Chiefly hunts small mammals; sometimes birds

● VOICE
Regular succession of short hoots

● HABITAT
Coniferous forests and (less commonly) mixed woodlands

● FLIGHT TIMES
Mainly active at night

● DISTRIBUTION
Around North Pole in Europe, North America and Asia, plus isolated populations in central and southern Europe; occasional visitor to Britain

● STATUS
Population density varies widely from one area to another, according to abundance of voles

were starting to make use of nestboxes provided for tree-nesting ducks such as goldeneye, they erected thousands of nestboxes throughout much of the conifer forest in Scandinavia and Finland. These were adopted with enthusiasm, and soon as many as 95 per cent of Tengmalm's owls were using the nestboxes – sometimes even those intended for starlings!

PROTECTING HER YOUNG

Incubation is carried out solely by the female, and her behaviour at the nest is rather different from that of the larger European owls. Instead of feigning injury or attacking intruders, she comes to the entrance of the nest, blocking the hole. This enables her to be alert to the approach of any predators such as pine martens, and also allows her to simply camouflage the nest hole with her plumage, which is a similar colour to the pine trunk. Both the parents feed the owlets, and unlike many other young owls, when they leave the nest they are fully able to fly.

Tengmalm's owl is another species which breeds all round the North Pole in Europe, Asia and North America. In seasons of vole scarcity a few of them may reach Britain, perhaps reaching double figures now and again, however they are unlikely ever to become resident here.

Scops owl – owl of the sunny south

This small owl mainly feeds on insects and other invertebrates, and is common in the warm lowlands of southern Europe. Its call is a clear whistle.

The facial disc is less distinct in this species of owl and the fringing ring of stiffer feathers is also not so conspicuous.

Although it is Europe's second smallest owl, the scops has a large wingspan for its size.

THE SCOPS OWL IS A DELIGHTFUL little bird, very different from many other European owls. At 19 cm it is the second smallest owl in Europe, and is a true migrant, breeding in the south and wintering in Africa, south of the Sahara. Some of them travel as much as 15,000 km from their breeding grounds to Africa and back again. Using fat stores for fuel, they lose up to 50 per cent of their average weight on the way. When they return to their breeding grounds in spring, they sometimes overshoot the mark and find themselves in Britain.

The scops has an unusual 'song', the musical bell-like sounds instantly conjuring up the atmosphere of a summer night in the Mediterranean. Neighbouring owls will adjust their calls so that each has its own distinctive sound. There may be five or six in an olive grove, sounding like a peal of bells. Sometimes the sound is confused with that of the midwife toad, which also calls at night.

A master of camouflage, the scops spends the day perched close to the trunk of a tree, unmoving and unseen. Its plumage is subtly coloured in shades of brown and grey which tone into the bark. But that's not all. The scops can also disguise its typical outline by stretching up into a thin elongated posture, narrowing its eyes to slits and broadening and flattening the area above its beak until it looks like a piece of bark. Once the transformation is complete, it will often 'freeze' in this position for minutes on end.

Other owls take insects as part of their diet, but the scops is by far the most insectivorous. Although it may take prey such as shrews and lizards, invertebrates can account for up to 94 per cent of its diet in the breeding season. Favourite breeding areas are stretches of open ground scattered with broad-leaved trees, such as orchards and parks.

Eggs are incubated by the female, and she stays in the nest while the young are small. The owlets' eyes begin to open on day three, and on day five they start the head-bobbing behaviour they use to beg for food when they leave the nest. The family stays together until migration, and the young become sexually mature on their return in spring.

SCOPS OWL FACT FILE

● **NAMES**
English name: Scops owl
Scientific name: *Otus scops*

● **SIZE**
19 cm;
approx. 90 g

● **KEY FEATURES**
Very small with eartufts, plumage overall greyish and sandy brown, eyes yellow; often adopts slim elongated posture

● **NEST**
Hole in tree or building, nestboxes

● **BREEDING**
Begins late April

● **EGGS**
4–5 eggs, incubated by female

● **YOUNG**
Leave nest at 21–29 days and start to fly immediately; independent 7–10 weeks

● **FOOD**
Chiefly large insects: crickets, moths, beetles, caterpillars etc; also earthworms

Short, rounded ear tufts may sometimes appear flattened sideways.

● **VOICE**
Bell-like 'chimes', frequently repeated

● **HABITAT**
Areas with scattered broad-leaved trees: orchards, olive groves, groups of palm trees, parks and gardens

● **FLIGHT TIMES**
Largely nocturnal, hunting at dawn and dusk

● **DISTRIBUTION**
Through much of southern Europe, parts of southern Russia and well into Asia; seldom reaches Britain

● **STATUS**
Depletion of fat reserves on migration may cause owls to be affected by pesticide sprays on insects they have eaten; many owls shot along migration route

Pygmy owl – the tiniest hunter

This tiny predator of the conifer forests has a dashing flight, often used to chase small birds in a manner more typical of a hawk than an owl.

A pygmy owl watches out for small mammals and then swoops down to catch them.

THE PYGMY OWL IS THE TINIEST of Europe's owls – barely larger than a house sparrow. Comparing this little bird with the massive eagle owl, it is hard to believe that they are both owls, but indeed both are fierce hunters. Generally the pygmy owl is active by day and it roosts by night. Its night vision is one of the poorest among owls – even poorer than human vision. In the far north however, where summer nights are light, it can see to hunt for longer. Typically, it is active from just before sunrise to just after sunset.

Over the course of a year, more than half of the pygmy owl's food consists of voles, the rest being mostly made up of various species of bird. Its hunting technique is based on surprise – it perches on the tip of a low tree until it sees a small animal moving on the woodland floor below, then glides out and drops onto it. If the first try fails it abandons the attempt; if successful it seizes the vole with both talons and paralyses it with a bite on the nose. Any surplus

BIRDS INTO OWLETS

Many types of owl are affected by the abundance or lack of voles and other animals that they feed on during the breeding season. The pygmy owl is also affected, but in a rather different way. Instead of wandering away from its normal breeding area in search of small mammals, it changes over to birds instead.

The pygmy is an amazingly skillful bird hunter. It takes at least 37 species – principally siskins, leaf warblers, chaffinches and pied fly catchers – often seizing them on the wing. It has even been known to catch larger birds such as great spotted woodpeckers, mistle thrushes and redwings – which in good condition are bigger than itself. The pygmy owl is such an effective hunter that it can almost wipe out the incubating small birds within range of its nest.

As the breeding season approaches however, a diet of birds doesn't make up for the absence of voles. The size of the pygmy owl's clutch is determined by the availability of voles shortly before laying, although some eggs will still be laid on the 'birds-only' diet. To produce a good-sized clutch and rear nestlings, the pygmy needs voles to feed on.

The pygmy owl is so small it is not easily spotted among dense forest foliage such as these pine needles.

PYGMY OWL FACT FILE

● **NAMES**
English name: Pygmy owl
Scientific name: *Glaucidium passerinum*

● **SIZE**
Average 16.5 cm; 60–75 g

● **KEY FEATURES**
Smallest owl of region; relatively small head, less well-marked facial disc than other owls; flicks tail like flycatcher; hunts mainly dawn and dusk

● **NEST**
Natural holes in trees, old woodpecker holes, nestboxes

● **BREEDING**
Start of breeding affected by weather; begins in April

● **EGGS**
Smallest egg of a European owl; 4–7 eggs; incubated by female 28–30 days

● **YOUNG**
Leave nest 30–35 days and start to fly immediately; independent 8–9 weeks

● **FOOD**
Mainly small mammals, plus wide variety of small birds

● **VOICE**
Very vocal; song like scops owl, often repeated

● **HABITAT**
Mature conifer forest; outside breeding season may move to deciduous woodland

● **FLIGHT TIMES**
Just before sunrise to just after sunset

● **DISTRIBUTION**
Northern Europe and Asia, plus small populations in central Europe; unlikely to be seen in Britain because of reluctance to cross water

● **STATUS**
Widespread but not abundant

White eyebrows and a stern expression characterise this tiny owl

food is stored on a forked twig or in a hole.

Pygmy owls live chiefly in northern conifer forests, and in the main mountain ranges of central Europe they remain on territory throughout the year. In winter however, Scandinavian owls often move nearer to human habitation where it is easier to find food. They can sometimes be seen chasing small birds on the wing around farmhouse gardens. Like larger owls, the pygmy's call and distinctive appearance attract the attention of its potential victims, and it is mobbed by chattering bands of small birds just as the tawny owl is.

Pygmy owls themselves are vulnerable to a whole range of enemies. As the smallest European owl it is on the menu of all of its larger cousins, especially the tawny and Ural owls. Martens will often invade nest holes and kill incubating females. Other animals also compete with the pygmy owl for desirable nest holes – the nuthatch may wall up a hole in the course of making its own nest while dormice block up holes with grass.

The pygmy owl occurs widely across Europe and Asia, although it is nowhere abundant. It has not been found in Britain, and because of its reluctance to cross water, we are unlikely to see it here.

Amazing owls around the world

We have a dozen splendid owls in Europe, but there are more than 100 species worldwide, in scorching deserts, humid swamps and freezing tundra – each with its own special fascination.

The burrowing owl can dig its own nest hole, but often shares with prairie dogs.

PEL'S FISHING OWL
Scotopelia peli

In Britain we don't normally associate owls with fishing, though tawny owls do catch fish. Elsewhere in the world there are a number of remarkable owls however, and perhaps the most magnificent is Pel's fishing owl. This is one of the biggest owls in the world, and it has a shaggy, loosely feathered head and rich rufous-coloured plumage.

Like other fishing owls, Pel's is adapted in several ways for catching fish. Its feet are bare of feathers and have sharp, spiny scales for gripping slippery fish. The facial disc is poorly defined, and this implies that its hearing is probably of little importance in catching underwater prey. Its heavy flapping flight – noisy compared with other owls – seems to confirm this.

Pel's fishing owls live along the forested banks of rivers, pools and swamps throughout most of Africa, south of the Sahara. They mainly hunt at night and prefer to fish over quiet pools and backwaters where they can detect the presence of fish by ripples in the surface of the water. The owl perches on a low branch or stump until it locates its prey, then swoops down – thrusting out its legs and talons, and closing its eyes at the point of impact. Usually it will complete a successful catch without dipping more than its feet into the water.

The owl can catch fish weighing up to two kilogrammes using this technique, though it often doesn't eat the whole animal. Returning to its perch it often consumes the real titbit, which is the head, and then discards the rest of the fish.

◄ *Unlike most owls, Pel's fishing owl is comparatively noisy in flight, as its underwater prey can't hear it coming.*

▼ *Many people think that the African white faced scops owl is the most beautiful, but there's a lot of competition.*

AFRICAN WHITE-FACED SCOPS OWL
Ptilopsis leucotis

Which is the most beautiful owl in the world? It's impossible to award a title, of course, as every owl has something to recommend it – from the magnificent eagle owl to the cute little scops. However, several authorities have independently suggested that the African white-faced scops owl might deserve the title of the 'most beautiful' or the 'most attractive'. This smallish owl – of a similar size to our familiar little owl – lives in the wide acacia savannahs of Africa. Here it preys on insects and rodents and nests in holes in trees, abandoned stick nests and even the domed nests of buffalo weavers.

So what is it that makes the little scops owl so special? Principally its remarkable orange eyes, which are surrounded by a large, white facial disc with dark edges. When this owl looks at you, you really know you've been looked at!

Which beautiful owl would get your vote?

BURROWING OWL
Speotyto cunicularia

Owls nest in tree holes, on cliffs, in hollows in the ground, in the old nests of other birds – and even underground. The burrowing owl has exceptionally long legs compared with other owls, and these come in useful for excavating nest holes. In other respects it looks much like a little owl and has the same comical habit of bobbing its head about when it is nervous.

This owl makes its nest in a roughly lined chamber at the end of a winding tunnel, about a metre underground. Here it lays up to 11 eggs – a larger clutch than most owls. The eggs are incubated by both parents and both feed the chicks on beetles and other large insects. But though burrowing owls can excavate their own tunnels, they often prefer to take advantage of those dug by mammals. In South America they might make their nests in the holes of viscachas (small, soft-furred rodents) or armadillos. In North America, they regularly move into prairie dog 'towns' –

Home in a cactus – the elf owl survives the heat of the desert by living in the cool interior of a local saguaro cactus.

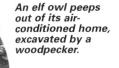

An elf owl peeps out of its air-conditioned home, excavated by a woodpecker.

Many owls have brilliantly coloured eyes, but the Verreaux's are dark brown. Its amazing pink eyelids make an eye-catching substitute.

busy colonies that can occupy several acres. But not all the neighbours are friendly, and they can include wolves, foxes, skunks and especially rattlesnakes. When owlets in the burrows are alarmed they make a hissing, rasping sound, very like a rattlesnake; their own special 'keep off' signal, perhaps?

ELF OWL
Micrathene whitneyi

Elf owls are tiny – they are in competition with a couple of other species for the title of 'smallest owl in the world'. They have round heads and bodies, no ear-tufts, prominent white eyebrows and a second set of 'pretend' eyebrows on the back of their heads to confuse predators.

Like many other owls, they usually nest in woodpeckers' holes, but these woodpecker holes are holes with a difference – excavated in the fluted columns of the saguaro cactus in the Sonora desert. In late March the saguaro is turgid from winter rains and the trunk expands and flattens, making it easy for the woodpecker to chisel into it. The bird pecks a few inches towards the centre of the cactus, then about 30 cm downwards to form a chamber. The cactus sap flowing around the chamber hardens into a tough woody lining, a 'saguaro boot' as it's called – a desirable residence for woodpeckers and then for elf owls.

The saguaro nest-hole is ideal for a pair of tiny owls trying to rear a family in the heat of the desert. To hatch successfully the eggs need to be maintained at about 38° C, but desert temperatures can reach 46° C at midday and vary by as much as 22° C over 24 hours. Fortunately for the elf owls, evaporation of moisture from the cactus during the day keeps the nest-hole 11° C cooler than the world outside. And at night the tonnes of fluid stored in the plant cool down slowly, maintaining the nest at 11° C above desert temperature.

In other words, the saguaro provides elf owls with something humans in the area might envy – natural air conditioning!

VERREAUX'S EAGLE OWL
Bubo lacteus

Verreaux's eagle owl is the largest African owl, and a powerful hunter. Mammals from vervet monkeys to tiny shrews come within its range, plus birds from the leggy secretary bird to the white eye. Even other owls and young hawks are sometimes snatched from the nest. Local people regard it as a bird of ill omen. If a Verreaux's owl hoots persistently near a village, people will move elsewhere. And if someone is 'owl-struck' – struck on the head by its powerful claws – no medicine is strong enough to ward off the evil effects. All the owl is doing, of course, is defending its nest from intruders coming too close.

The Verreaux's most remarkable features are its eyelids. Those of the adult and even the young owlet in the nest are a bright shade of pink. Why should this be? It's been suggested that these colourful eyelids might play a part in a courtship or territorial display. While most owls have brilliant orange or yellow eyes, the Verreaux's are dark brown and melancholy, so perhaps the pink eyelids are a signalling substitute.

FOREST OWLET
Athene blewitti

A hundred years ago a new species of owl was discovered in the damp, tropical forests of north India. It was named *Athene blewitti* – the forest owlet. It was a small owl, stocky and short-winged, and distinguished from a similar species in the area by its solid brown breast, pale face, larger bill and gleaming white legs. Several skins were collected, and for many years it vanished into oblivion. After unsuccessful searches in 1975 and 1976 it was concluded that it was probably extinct.

Then, near the end of 1997, two American ornithologists from the Smithsonian Institute made an expedition to look for the owl in areas where it had been seen before. At first news was not good, as the high forests had mainly been destroyed. But they persisted in their search, and almost at the end of the trip they sighted not one, but two owlets – rediscovered after more than a century!

AMAZING OWLS

- **LARGEST**
  European eagle owl (northern race)
- **SMALLEST**
  Several candidates, including elf owl
- **KILLS MOST OTHER OWLS**
  European eagle owl; in Britain, tawny owl
- **MASTER OF DISGUISE**
  European scops, long-eared or flammulated owl
- **LIVES MAINLY ON INSECTS**
  European scops
- **LIVES LARGELY ON FISH**
  Pel's fishing owl
- **FOUND IN HOLES IN THE GROUND**
  Burrowing owl
- **LIVES IN CACTUS**
  Elf owl

- **MOST BEAUTIFUL**
  African white-faced scops owl
- **MOST INTERNATIONAL**
  Barn owl
- **RAREST**
  Several owls are only known from a few specimens obtained many years ago, but sometimes they turn up again
- **REDISCOVERED OWL**
  Indian forest owlet

Usually the flammulated owl looks typically owl-like, but it will stretch up tall and thin when it wants to disguise itself – as do the long-eared owl and European scops.

INDEX

Picture acknowledgments

Cover: Phil Bricknell, BC/Kim Taylor, NP/E.A. Janes, Mike Read **1:** Mike Read **3:** Paul Bricknell **5:** Paul Bricknell **6:** NP/S.C Bisserot, NP/W.S. Paton, NP/Geoff Du Feu **7:** BC/Dennis Green, NP/E. A. Janes, NP/Frank B. Blackburn **8:** NP/Don Smith, NP/E.A. Janes **9:** BC/Kim Taylor, BBC/David Welling, NP/Geoff Du Feu, BIOFOTOS/Jason Venus **10:** BC/William S. Paton, FLPA/S. Maslowski, NP/Frank B. Blackburn, NHPA/Walter Murray **11:** NP/Roger Tidman, NP/Hugh Clark, NP/Geoff Du Feu **12:** NP/Don Smith, NP/Colin Carver **13:** BBC/Mike Wilkes, BC/Hans Reinhard, FLPA/W. Wisniewski, BBC/Paul N. Johnson **14:** NHPA/Stephen Dalton **15:** Mike Read **16:** NHPA/Alan Williams, Mike

Read **17:** NHPA/E.A. James **18:** Mike Read, BC/Hans Reinhard **19:** Mike Read, Biofotos/JasonVenus, BC/Kim Taylor **20:** BC/Hans Reinhard, BC/George McCarthy **21:** Paul Bricknell **22:** NHPA/Michael Leach, NHPA/Stephen Dalton **23:** BC/George McCarthy, BC/W.S. Paton **24:** BC/Hans Reinhard **25:** BC/George McCarthy, BC/Janos Jurka, NHPA/Paal Hermansen, BC/Allan G. Potts, BC/Kim Taylor **26:** NHPA/Michael Leach, BC/Kim Taylor, NHPA/Andy Rouse **27:** BC/Hans Reinhard, NHPA/John Buckingham **28:** NHPA/Manfred Danegger, NHPA/Stephen Dalton **29:** BC/Jan Van De Kam, Heather Angel **30:** NHPA/Dr. Eckart Pott, BC/Hans Reinhard, BC/Paul

Van Gaalen **31:** BC/Werner Layer, NHPA/Jany Sauvanet, NHPA/Robert Erwin **32:** NHPA/Melvin Grey, BC/Hans Reinhard, NHPA/Alan Williams **33:** NHPA/Alan Williams, NHPA/Michael Leach, BC/Erwin & Peggy Bauer **34:** FLPA/W. Wisniewski, FLPA/R. Tidman, FLPA/M. Callan **35:** FLPA/E. & D. Hosking, FLPA/S. Maslowski, FLPA/W. Wisniewski **36:** FLPA/W. Wisniewski, FLPA/E. & D. Hosking, FLPA/S. Maslowski **37:** FLPA/Brake/Sunset, FLPA/R. Austing **38:** BC/Stephen J. Krasemann **39:** BBC/Dietmar Nill, BC/Hans Reinhard, BC/William S. Paton **40:** BC/Tom Schandy, FLPA/Don Smith **41:** BC/Paul Van Gaalen, BC/Werner Layer, BC/Uwe Walz **42:** BC/Erwin & Peggy Bauer,

BC/Robert P. Carr, BBC/Nigel Tucker **43:** BC/Gunter Ziesler, BC/Erwin & Peggy Bauer **44:** BC/Hans Reinhard, BBC/Bengt Lundberg **45:** BBC/Seppo Valjakka, BBC/Bengt Lundberg **46:** BBC/Steven David Miller, BC/Gerald Cubitt, FLPA/E & D. Hosking **47:** BC/Jen & Des Bartlett, BC/Luiz Claudio Marigo, BC/Erwin & Peggy Bauer

NP = Nature Photographers, BC = Bruce Coleman, BBC = BBC Natural History Unit, FLPA = Frank Lane Picture Agency, NHPA = Natural History Photographic Agency

Illustrations:
16-17, 22-23, 29: A/W John Ridyard